Nelson *Mathematics* 2

Activity Book

Series Authors and Senior Consultants
Marian Small • Mary Lou Kestell

Senior Author
Heather Kelleher

Grade 2 Author Team Leader
Joanne Simmons

Assessment Consultants
Joanne Simmons • Damian Cooper

NELSON / EDUCATION

NELSON / EDUCATION

Nelson Mathematics 2
Activity Book

Series Authors and Senior Consultants
Marian Small, Mary Lou Kestell

Senior Author
Heather Kelleher

Grade 1 Author Team Leader
Karen LaRone

Grade 2 Author Team Leader
Joanne Simmons

Authors
Karen Chong, Anna Jupp,
Karen LaRone, Norma MacFarlane,
Janice Novakowski, Joanne Simmons

Assessment Consultants
Joanne Simmons, Damian Cooper

Associate Vice President of Publishing
David Steele

Senior Publisher, Mathematics
Beverley Buxton

Senior Program Manager
Shirley Barrett

First Folio ResourceGroup, Inc.:
Program Manager
Fran Cohen

Senior Developmental Editor
Susan Petersiel Berg

Developmental Editors
Susan Hughes
Sarah Mawson
Brenda McLoughlin
Amanda Stewart

Executive Managing Editor,
Development & Testing
Cheryl Turner

Executive Managing Editor, Production
Nicola Balfour

Production Editors
Susan Aihoshi
Gary Burford

Editorial Assistant
Megan Robinson

Senior Production Coordinator
Sharon Latta Paterson

Creative Director
Angela Cluer

Art Director
Ken Phipps

Art Management
ArtPlus Ltd.: Donna Guilfoyle,
Joelle Cottle, Kyle Gell

Illustrators
ArtPlus, Maryann Kovalski, Bill Suddick,
Sacha Warunkiw

Interior Design
Peggy Rhodes

Cover Design
Suzanne Peden

Cover Image
Christoph Burki/Stone/Getty Images

Composition
ArtPlus Ltd.

Printer
Globus

National Library of Canada Cataloguing
in Publication

Nelson Mathematics 2: Activity book /
Marian Small ... [et al.].

Includes index.
For use in grade 2.

ISBN 0-17-626091-9

1. Mathematics—Problems, exercises, etc.
I. Small, Marian II. Title: Nelson
mathematics two.

QA135.6.N442 2004 Suppl. 1
510   C2004-903796-X

Contents

CHAPTER 1   Sorting and Patterning   2

CHAPTER 2   Number to 50   12

CHAPTER 3   Data Management   20

CHAPTER 4   Addition and Subtraction Strategies   30

CHAPTER 5   Linear Measurement   41

CHAPTER 6   Place Value   54

CHAPTER 7   2-D Geometry   67

CHAPTER 8   Two-Digit Addition and Subtraction   80

CHAPTER 9   Multiplication and Division   94

CHAPTER 10   Measuring Time and Money   105

CHAPTER 11   3-D Geometry and Measurement   117

CHAPTER 12   Fractions   129

CHAPTER 13   Probability   139

CHAPTER 14   Patterns   152

GLOSSARY   161

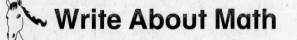 **Write About Math**

Draw 2 patterns. How do you know
they are patterns?

I can see a pattern on:

Here is a picture of the pattern:

One thing I know about patterns is:

Grids

⬤ My pattern core looks like this:

Here is my pattern in rows of 5.

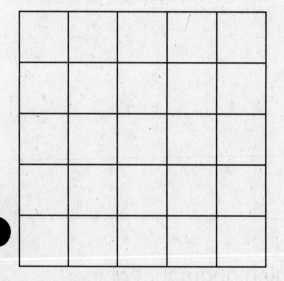

Here is my pattern in rows of 8.

Glossary Words

pattern core

The **pattern core** is the part of a pattern that keeps repeating.
Draw the pattern core from this pattern:

attribute

An **attribute** of an object tells something about that object.

Some attributes of this button are its:
    colour (it is grey)
    shape (it is round)

Another attribute of a button could be:

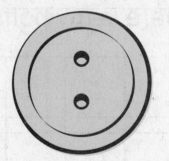

Sorting Stickers Table

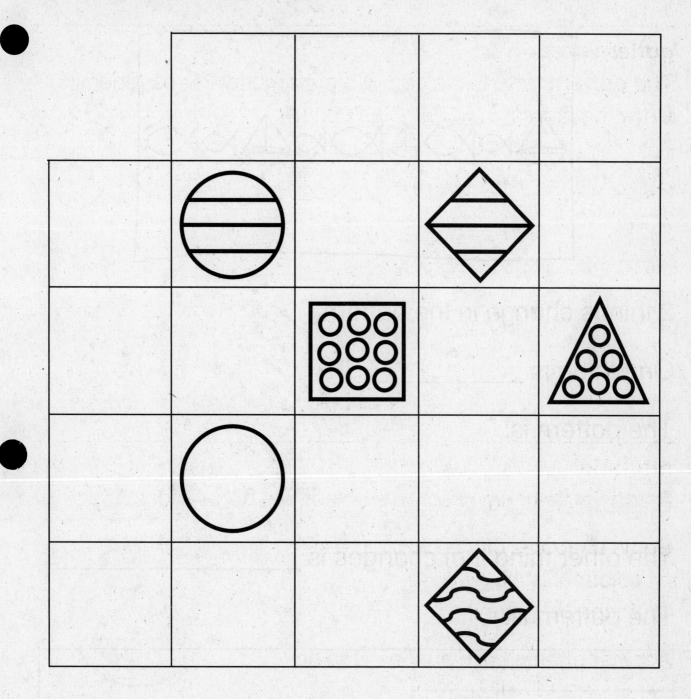

Describing a Pattern

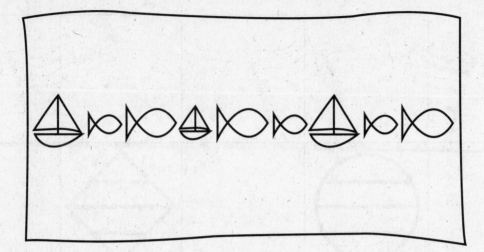

2 things change in the pattern.

One thing is _____.

The pattern is:

The other thing that changes is _____.

The pattern is:

Communication Checklist

❏ Did you use math
   language?

❏ Did you give enough
   information?

Chapter 1 Lesson 4

Describing a Pattern 2

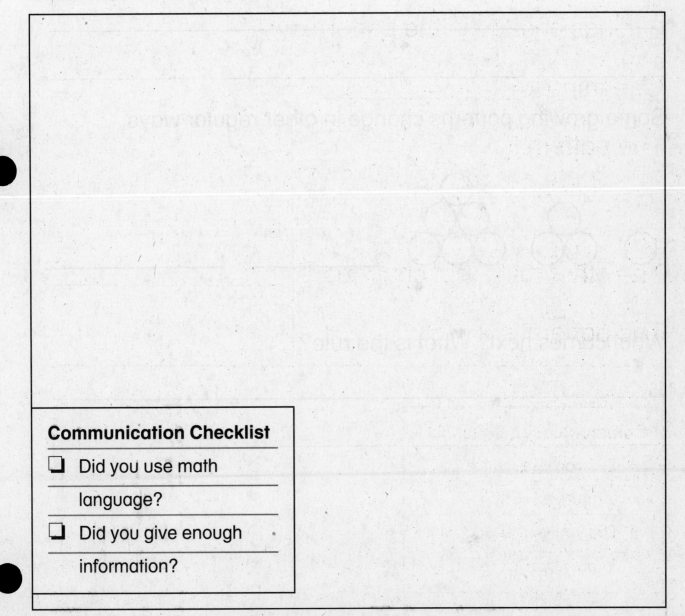

Tell about the pattern.

Communication Checklist

❑ Did you use math language?

❑ Did you give enough information?

Glossary Words

growing pattern

Growing patterns change in some sort of regular way.

Some growing patterns change by adding or subtracting the same number over and over.

5, 10, 15, 20, _____

What comes next? What is the rule?

_____

_____

Some growing patterns change in other regular ways.

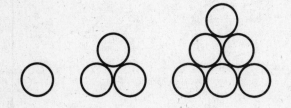 _____ _____

What comes next? What is the rule?

_____

_____

I'm a Math Thinker

⬤ Colour and write to show the math thinking you used.

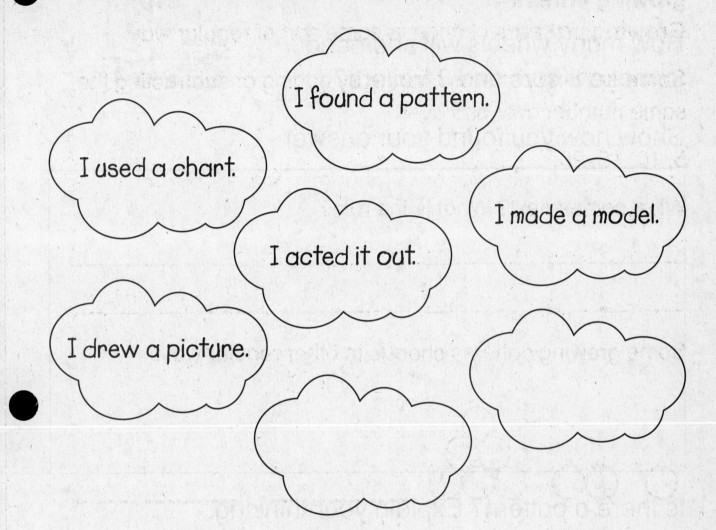

I found a pattern.

I used a chart.

I made a model.

I acted it out.

I drew a picture.

Show how you solved the problem.

Chapter 1 Lesson 7   Activity 1.8   **9**

How Many Wheels?

Sam is making cars and trailers.

How many wheels will she need to make 8 cars and 8 trailers?

Show how you found your answer.

Is there a pattern? Explain your thinking.

I used
- ☐ pictures
- ☐ numbers
- ☐ words

Chapter 1 Chapter Task

Thinking Back

● Choose 2 shapes. Choose 2 colours.

Make a pattern with your shapes and colours.

What comes next? How do you know?

Write About Math

How I use numbers:

What I know about 10s and 1s:

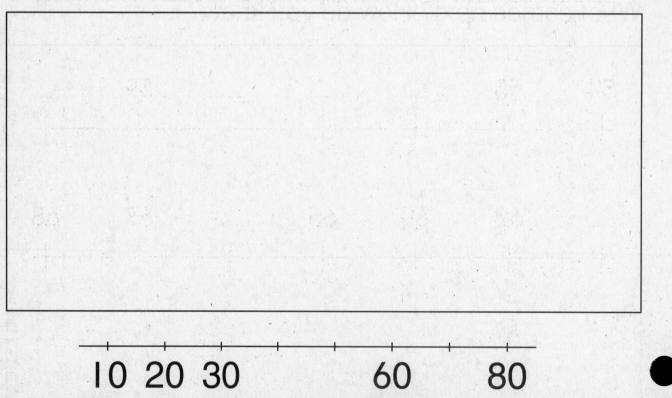

10 20 30   60   80

Number Line Puzzles

● Print the missing numbers on each number line. Circle the ones that would be in your skip-counting pattern.

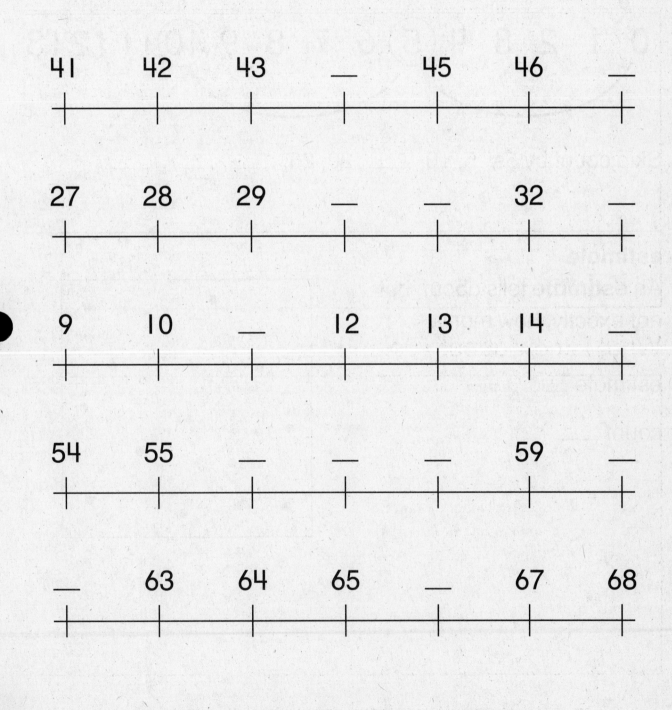

41   42   43   __   45   46   __

27   28   29   __   __   32   __

● 9   10   __   12   13   14   __

54   55   __   __   __   59   __

__   63   64   65   __   67   68

Chapter 2 Lesson 2   Activity 2.2

Glossary Words

skip count

When we **skip count**, we count by leaving out the same size group of numbers each time.

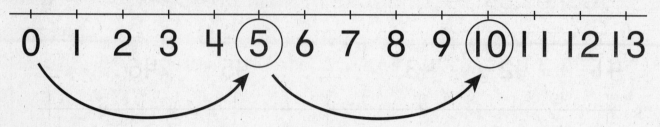

Skip count by 5s: 5, 10, ____, 20, 25, ____, ____, ____

---

estimate

An **estimate** tells about, but not exactly, how many.

estimate ____

count ____

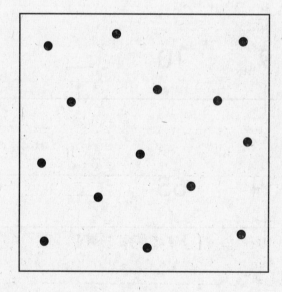

How Many Socks?

● How many socks are the students in your class wearing today? _____

Show the number of socks in 4 different ways.

Write a number that is greater than the number of socks. _____

Show that number 4 different ways. Use the back of this page or another piece of paper.

Comparing Numbers

Use 10-frames to show which number is greater.

Mark each number on the number line.
Then circle the greater number in each box.

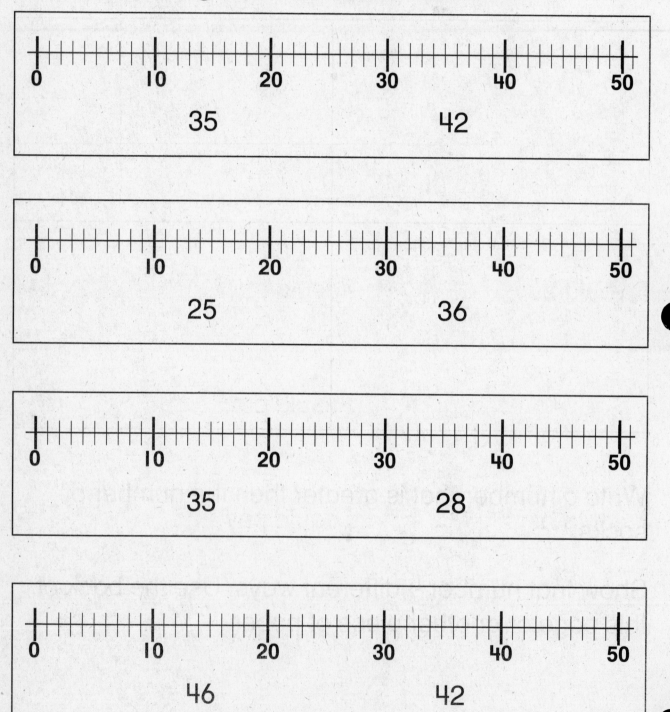

Chapter 2 Lesson 5

Buying Stickers

Super Stickers

I would buy: I could pay:

I could pay:

I would buy: I could pay:

I could pay:

Who Collected More?

2 children collected leaves.
One child collected 34 leaves.
One child collected 43 leaves.

Draw a sketch of how you showed the 2 numbers.
Explain how you know who collected more.

I used

☐ pictures

☐ numbers

☐ words

Chapter 2 Chapter Task

Thinking Back

● Finish these skip-counting patterns.
Tell how you counted.

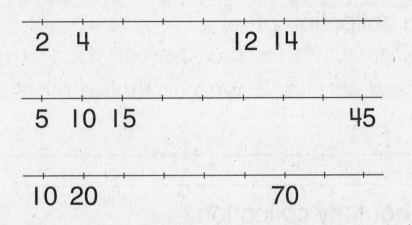

2   4   12 14

5 10 15   45

10 20   70

Here are some ways I can show what I know
about a 2-digit number.

🐴 Write About Math

I have a collection of

Facts about my collection

1	2
3	4

These fit in my collection:

because:

About My Graph

● The title of my graph is _____

_____

My labels are _____

_____

Here are 4 things my graph tells me.

Glossary Words

data

Data is another word for information.

Sometimes we show data in graphs, tables, and charts.

What data would you give to answer the question:
What are the ages of your family members?_____

pictograph

A **pictograph** uses _____
to show data.

Finish the pictograph to show that
3 people have cats, 1 has a fish,
4 have no pets, and 5 have dogs.

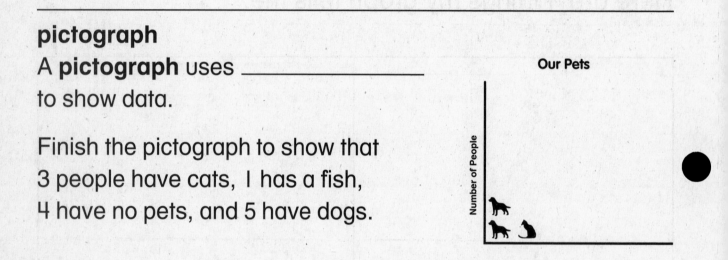

Our Pets

bar graph

A **bar graph** uses bars to show data.

This bar graph shows that _____ people said that yellow is their favourite _____.

It also shows that _____
_____.

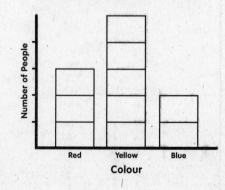

Favourite Primary Colours

Chapter 3 Lessons 3 and 5

Conducting a Survey

Survey question:

| |
| |

What I found out:

Choices	Tally	Total

The survey shows that:

| |
| |

Make a graph to show your survey results.
Use another sheet of paper.

Glossary Words

survey

We use a **survey** to get information by asking people questions.

An example of a survey question is:

Which Graph Matches?

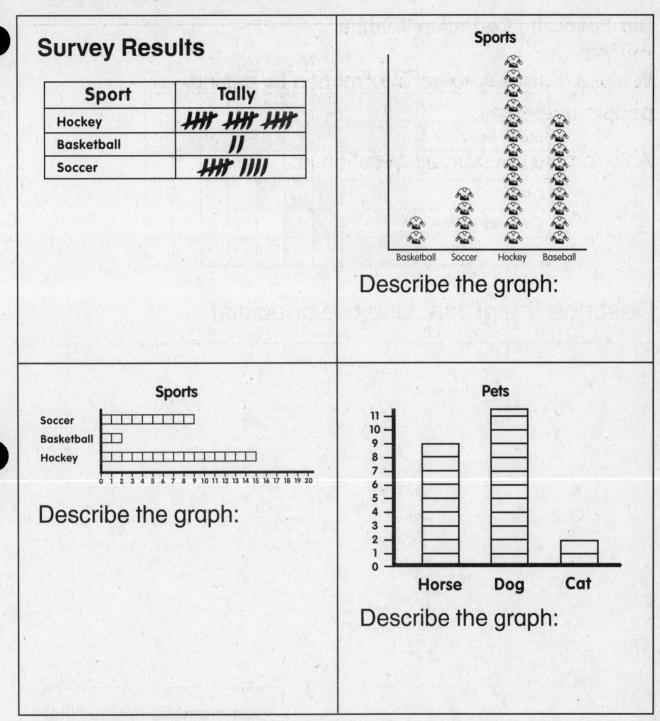

Survey Results

Sport	Tally
Hockey	~~IIII~~ ~~IIII~~ ~~IIII~~
Basketball	II
Soccer	~~IIII~~ IIII

Sports

Basketball Soccer Hockey Baseball

Describe the graph:

Sports

Soccer
Basketball
Hockey

0 1 2 3 4 5 6 7 8 9 10 11 12 13 14 15 16 17 18 19 20

Describe the graph:

Pets

11
10
9
8
7
6
5
4
3
2
1
0

Horse   Dog   Cat

Describe the graph:

Which graph shows the survey results?
Turn over the page (or use another sheet of paper)
and explain how you know.

Describing a Graph

Our Favourite Canadian Wildlife

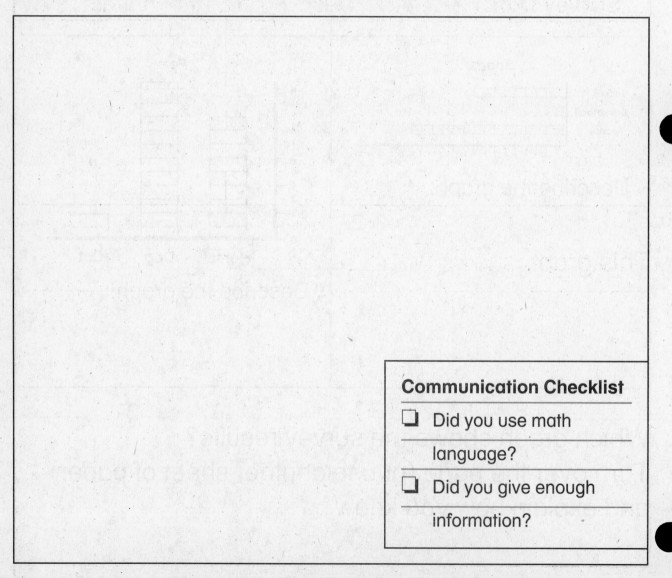

Name of Animal	Number of People									
	1	2	3	4	5	6	7	8	9	10
Fox										
Black bear										
Wolf										
Otter										
Canada goose										
Other										

Describe the graph. Use the checklist.

Communication Checklist

❑ Did you use math language?

❑ Did you give enough information?

Gathering Data

Survey question:

What I found out:

Survey Data	Tally	Total

This graph shows what I found out.

Using Data to Solve a Problem

Describe your graph. Use math words.

How can your information help the planners solve their problem?

Chapter 3 Chapter Task

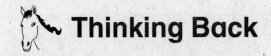
Thinking Back

Toys	Tally
Cars	||
Action figures	~~||||~~
Puzzles	|||

What question do you think Jonathan asked?

Display the information a different way.

Explain why this is a good way to show what Jonathan found out.

Chapter 3 Chapter Task   Activity 3.10   **29**

Write About Math

These are numbers that are important to me.

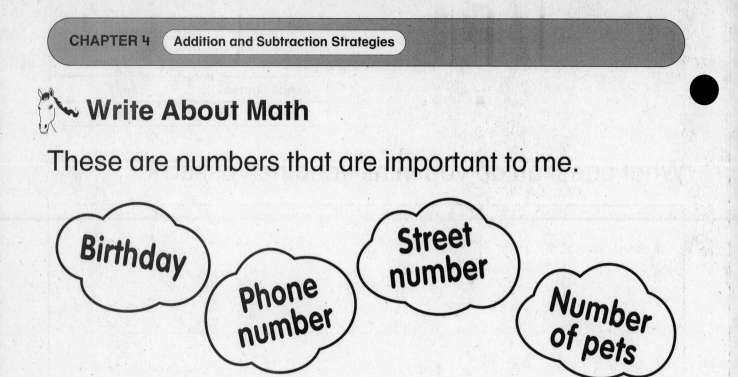

Tell some addition and subtraction stories with those numbers.

Pet Store Stories

● Draw a pet store picture.

Write some addition stories to go with your picture.

Write some subtraction stories to go with
your picture.

Glossary Words

sum

When we add, we join parts together to find out how much is in the whole amount. The whole amount is called the **sum**.

Draw 2 different ways to find the sum of 7 + 8.

| | |
| | |

fact family

A **fact family** is a group of facts. Each fact uses the same numbers.

These 4 facts make a fact family.

$$3 + 5 = 8 \quad 8 - 5 = 3$$
$$5 + 3 = 8 \quad 8 - 3 = 5$$

Make a fact family using the numbers 2, 4, and 6.

How Many Cubes?

● How many cubes do you need to make a 10-step staircase?

Show how to use addition to find your answer.

●

●

●

I used

☐ pictures

☐ numbers

☐ words

Triangle Doubles Plus One

Draw pictures to show the triangles
you made.

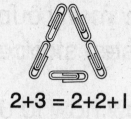

$2+3 = 2+2+1$

Write a number sentence
to describe each triangle.

Chapter 4 Lesson 3

Solving Addition Problems with 10-Frames

⬤ Use your 10-frames to figure out the answer to these problems:

$7 + 5 =$ ___ $8 + 6 =$ ___ $9 + 7 =$ ___

$7 + 4 =$ ___ $6 + 7 =$ ___ $8 + 5 =$ ___

$9 + 8 =$ ___ $4 + 9 =$ ___

Show some ways someone can figure out the answer for $7 + 8 =$ ___.

Pattern-Block Drop

Draw pattern blocks with a total of 22 sides.

Tell how you solved the problem.
Show how you know your answer is correct.

I used

☐ pictures

☐ numbers

☐ words

Buying Pet Supplies

You and 2 friends are each buying something for a pet. You each have $10 to spend. Show what each one can buy.

Write a number sentence to show how much each person has left.

Person 1

Person 2

Person 3

Fact Families

Use counters to find a fact family for each of the houses. Write the fact family.

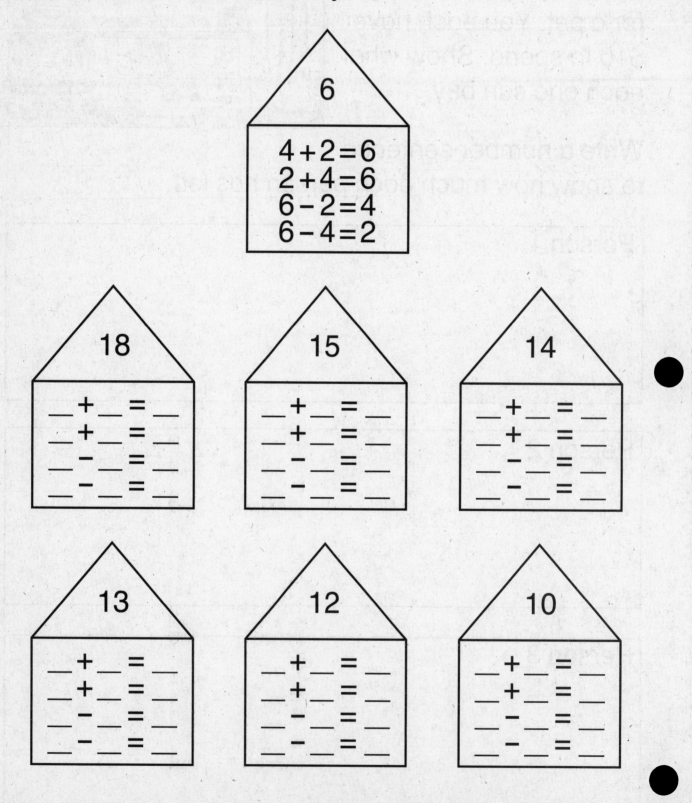

6

4 + 2 = 6
2 + 4 = 6
6 − 2 = 4
6 − 4 = 2

18

__ + __ = __
__ + __ = __
__ − __ = __
__ − __ = __

15

__ + __ = __
__ + __ = __
__ − __ = __
__ − __ = __

14

__ + __ = __
__ + __ = __
__ − __ = __
__ − __ = __

13

__ + __ = __
__ + __ = __
__ − __ = __
__ − __ = __

12

__ + __ = __
__ + __ = __
__ − __ = __
__ − __ = __

10

__ + __ = __
__ + __ = __
__ − __ = __
__ − __ = __

How Many Trips?

⬤ How many trips will it take to get 22 children and their teacher to the pet store? Use words, numbers, and pictures to explain your answer.

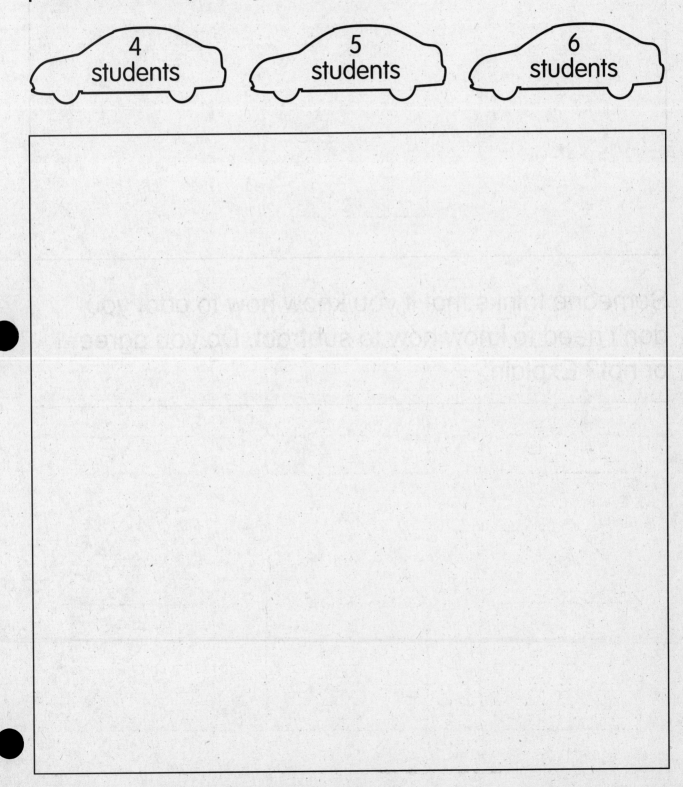

Here are some different ways to add 8 + 5.

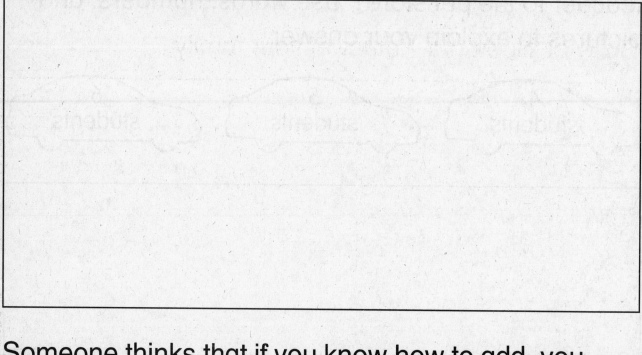

Someone thinks that if you know how to add, you don't need to know how to subtract. Do you agree or not? Explain.

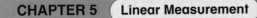

Write About Math

Draw or glue on a picture of your family.

_____ is taller than _____.

_____ is shorter than _____.

What else can you tell about the heights?

Glossary Words

height

When you measure **height**, you measure how tall something is, from top to bottom or bottom to top.

The _____ is taller than
the _____ .
The dog is _____ than
the _____ .

length

When you measure **length**, you measure how long something is, from beginning to end.

The _____ is longer than the _____ .
The turtle is _____ than the _____ .

Handy Measuring

● What can you find that is 10 hand widths long?
Estimate and then measure to check.

I think this might be 10 hand widths long.	Measurement

Which estimate was closest to 10 hand widths?

Penny Flicks

1. I think I can flick a penny this far: _____ cm.

2. Flick 5 times. Record the results.

Try number	I estimated	I measured
1		
2		
3		
4		
5		

3. My longest flick was _____ cm.

4. Draw a line to show your shortest flick.

5. How did you draw your line?

Chapter 5 Lesson 3

Glossary Words

centimetre

A **centimetre** is a unit of measure.

You can use centimetres to measure a _____.

A line that is 1 centimetre long looks like this:

A line that is 10 centimetres long looks like this:

The symbol for centimetres is _____.

---

metre

A **metre** is 100 centimetres long.

You can use metres to measure a _____.

The symbol for metres is _____.

---

perimeter

The **perimeter** is the distance around a shape or object.

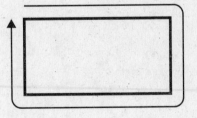

The perimeter of this shape is _____ cm.

Metre Search

Find at least one distance that fits in each category.

Category	What we found
Between 1 m and 2 m	
Between 3 m and 5 m	
Between 5 m and 7 m	
More than 10 m	

If we have centimetres to measure with, why do we need metres, too?

Chapter 5 Lesson 4

Telling about Sizes

tall   short   wide   long   thin

How can you sort things in the classroom?

Draw 3 things in each box.

_____ things	_____ things

Choose one thing from each box.
Use math words to tell about its size.

Cake Perimeters

Cake Picture	Estimated Perimeter	Perimeter Measure

Why do you have to remember where you started when you measure the perimeter?

Chapter 5 Lesson 6

I'm a Math Thinker

● Colour and write to show the math thinking you used.

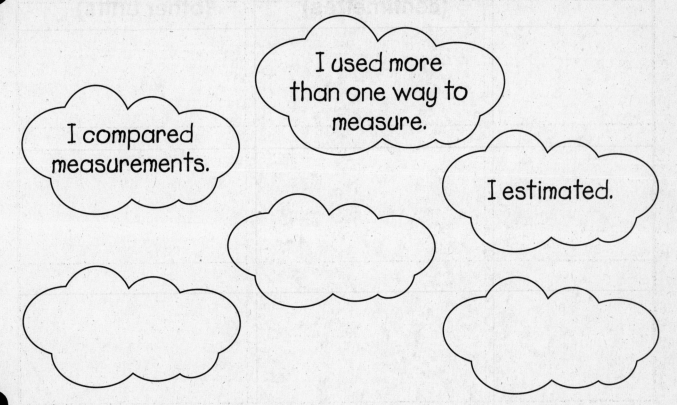

I compared measurements.

I used more than one way to measure.

I estimated.

● Write to explain a good way to measure a cake top. What tool should someone use? Explain your choices.

How Far Around?

Container	Distance around (centimetres)	Distance around (other units)

Circle the container with the longest distance around.
Tell how you know.

Chapter 5 Lesson 7

Making Shapes

 Draw a square with 10 centimetre sides.

On the back of the page or another piece of paper, draw a rectangle of any size.

Measuring the Perimeter of Shapes

Look at the shapes you drew on Activity 5.11.
Which shape has a longer perimeter?
Show how you found out.

Cut a 1 metre string. Will it wrap once, twice, or more than twice around each shape? Explain how you know.

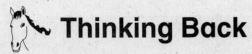

Thinking Back

● What did you learn about measuring?

Draw someone who is using a measuring tool.

Write About Math

A number between 10 and 100 that is important to me is _____.

This number is important because:

This picture shows how many things my number stands for.

Comparing Handfuls

● Take a handful of buttons and a handful of cubes.
Which handful has more?

Try the experiment 3 times.
Record the results in the chart.
Each time, circle the number that is more.

Experiment	How many buttons?	How many cubes?
1		
2		
3		

If I did this experiment again, I think I would get
between _____ and _____ buttons.
I think I would get between _____ and _____ cubes.
I think I would get more _____
because _____
_____.

Close to 50

What can you find that's close to 50 ones long?

What we measured	Length in ones	Length	
		Tens	**Ones**

The length we found that was the closest to 50 ones was _____.

What's Your Number?

● Draw blocks.
Show your number 3 ways.

Glossary Words

digit

The numbers from 0 to 9 are called **digits**.
We write all the numbers in our number system
with these digits.

In greater numbers, the
tens digit tells how many
full 10-frames there are in
a number. The **ones digit**
tells how many extra ones
there are.

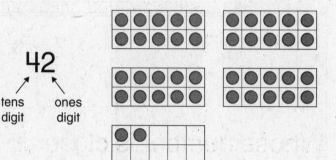

Mark a number in the 20s on this number line.

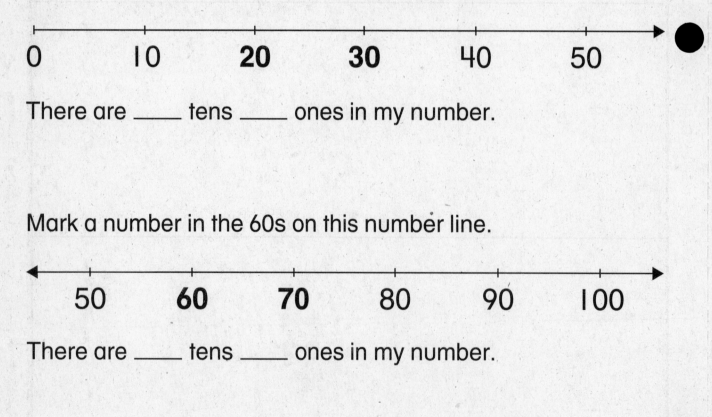

0   10   **20**   **30**   40   50

There are _____ tens _____ ones in my number.

Mark a number in the 60s on this number line.

50   **60**   **70**   80   90   100

There are _____ tens _____ ones in my number.

Who Is Closer to 50?

● My roll: _____   My partner's roll: _____

Show where you think the numbers go on the number line.

0   50   100

Whose number is closer to 50? Show how you know.

Spinning Sums

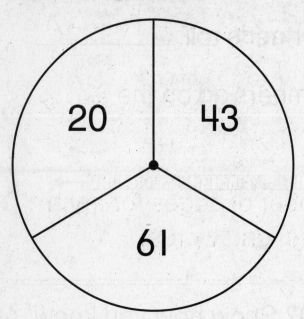
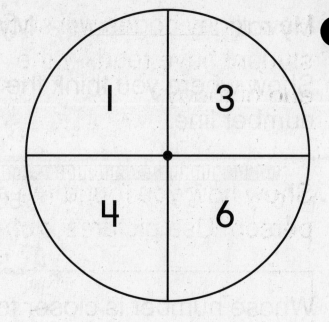

Spin both spinners.
Add the numbers you spun.
What sums are possible?

Print one number sentence you could spin.
Show 2 ways to check your adding.

_____ + _____ = _____

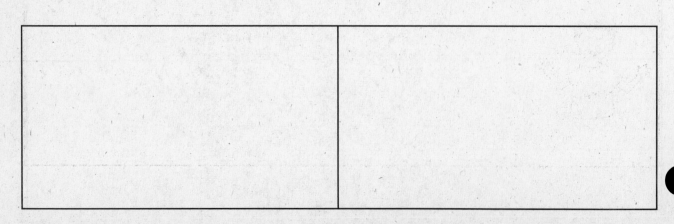

The Read-a-thon

How many pages will each student have read by the end of today?

Show how you found the number of pages for each person. Use pictures, numbers, and words.

I'm a Math Thinker

Colour and write to show how you solved the problem.

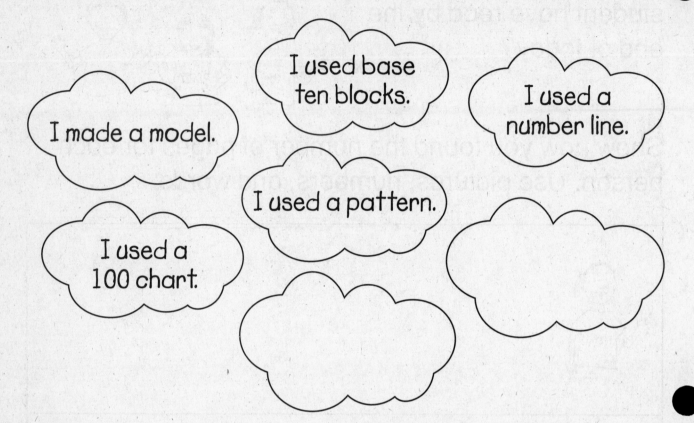

I made a model.

I used base ten blocks.

I used a number line.

I used a pattern.

I used a 100 chart.

Show how to solve one of the problems a different way.

Calculator Checkup

I tried to subtract 39 − 4.
Does my calculator show the right answer? _____
Show how you know.

I tried to subtract 56 − 2.
Does my calculator show the right answer? _____
Show how you know.

I tried to subtract 67 − 5.
Does my calculator show the right answer? _____
Show how you know.

Subtraction Action

Show how to solve each problem.

I have 50¢. I want to buy . How much money will I have left?

I have 80¢. I want to buy 8¢. How much money will I have left?

I have 75¢. I want to buy 9¢. How much money will I have left?

Make up your own yard-sale problem.
Show how to solve it.

How Many to Tie?

RED BLUE
45 36

● Choose your favourite team.
Show the team's score
3 different ways.

● Red has 45 points and Blue has 36 points. How many
more points does Blue need to score to tie the game?
Show how you got your answer.

I used

☐ pictures

☐ numbers

☐ words

Chapter 6 Chapter Task   Activity 6.12

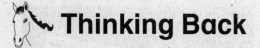
Choose a number between 30 and 100.
Show your number 4 different ways.

What number would you have to add to your number
to get to the next 10? Show how you know.

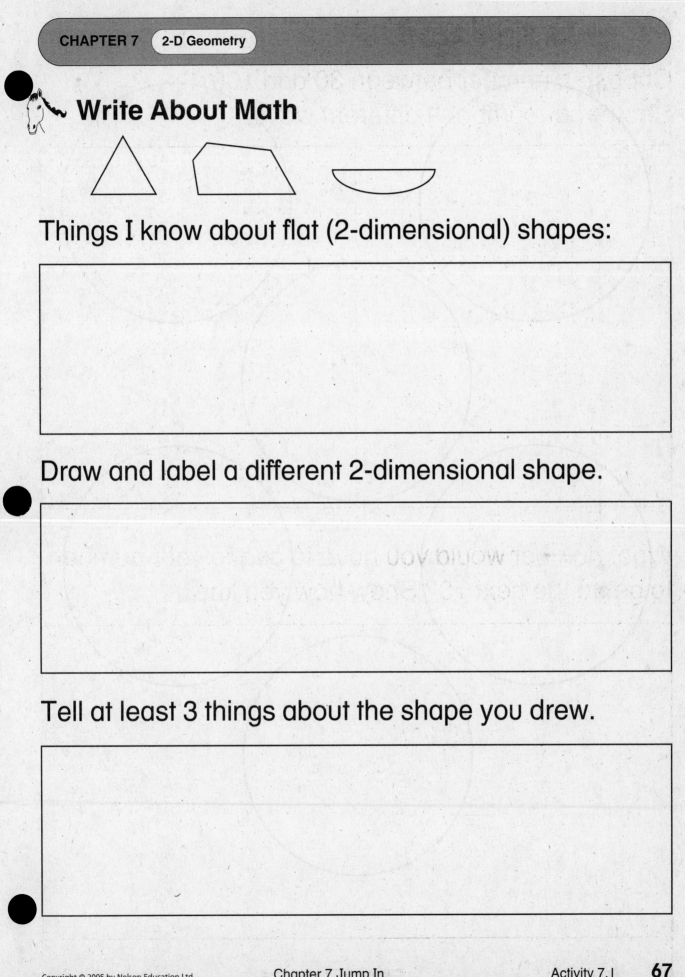

Write About Math

Things I know about flat (2-dimensional) shapes:

Draw and label a different 2-dimensional shape.

Tell at least 3 things about the shape you drew.

Circles for Making Shapes

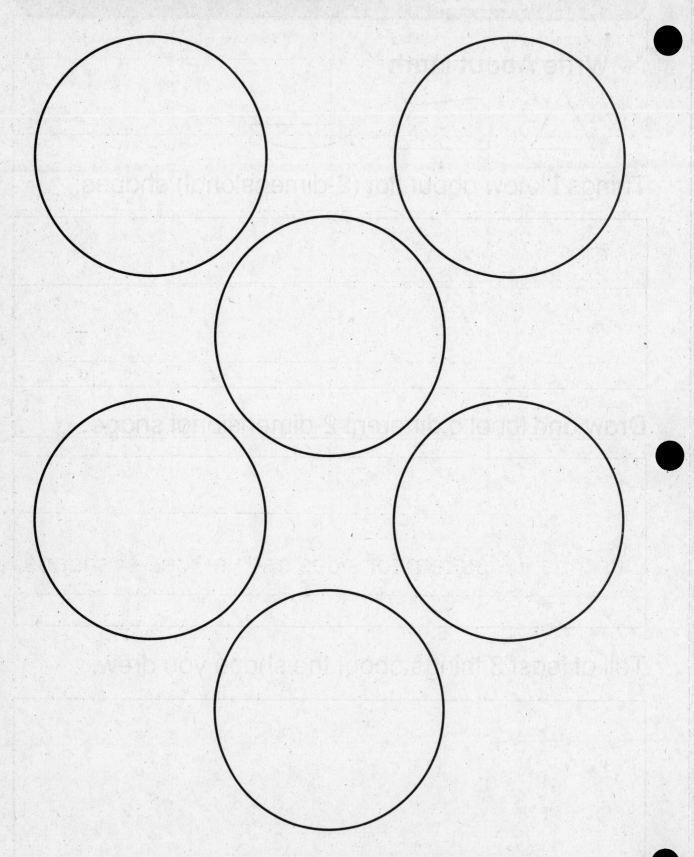

Sorting 2-D Shapes

Shape Name	Sides	Vertices	Draw
triangle			
quadrilateral			
pentagon			
hexagon			
heptagon			
octagon			

Describe the pattern for sides and vertices of shapes.

Communicating about 2-D Shapes

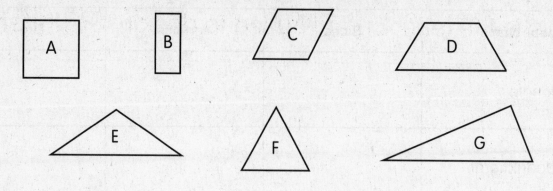

My shape clues:

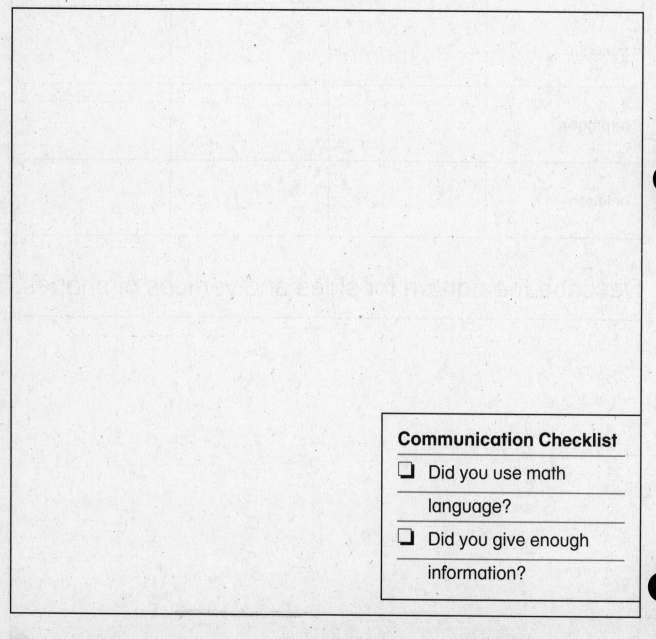

Communication Checklist

❑ Did you use math language?

❑ Did you give enough information?

Patterns with Flips and Turns

 This is the letter cutout I used to design my pattern:

This is how I made the pattern:

Kitchen Map

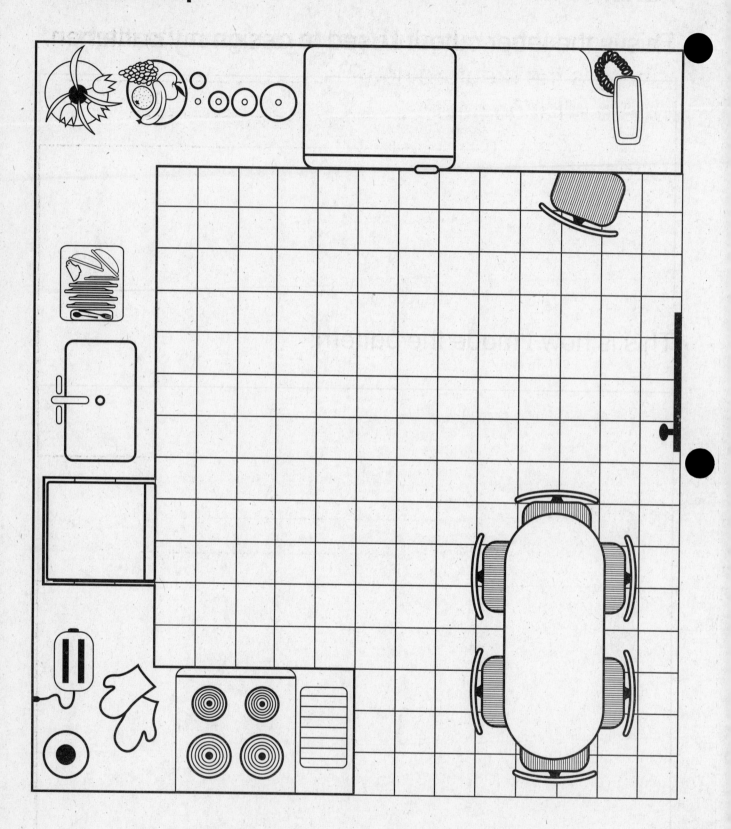

Chapter 7 Lesson 7

Finding the Way

● Help your shape creature get to places in the kitchen.
Where is the creature now? _____
Where will it go next? _____

Directions:

●

Where is it now? _____
Where will it go next? _____

Directions:

●

Chapter 7 Lesson 7

Glossary Words

We can move things in different ways.

---

slides

If you **slide** a shape, it looks the same. It just moves to a different place.

Slide and Trace

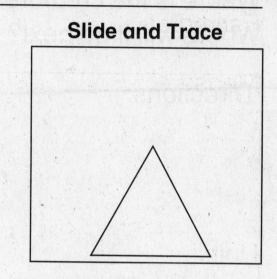

---

turns

If you **turn** a shape, it spins around a point.

Turn and Trace

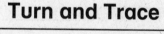

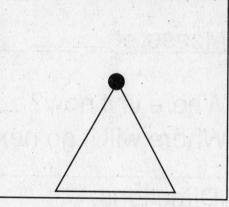

---

flips

If you **flip** a shape, it flips across a line.

Flip and Trace

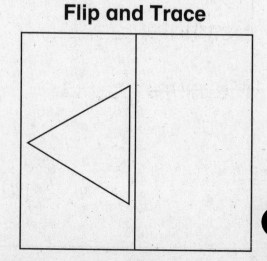

Measuring Area with Pattern Blocks

Unit: _____

Estimate: _____

Measure: _____

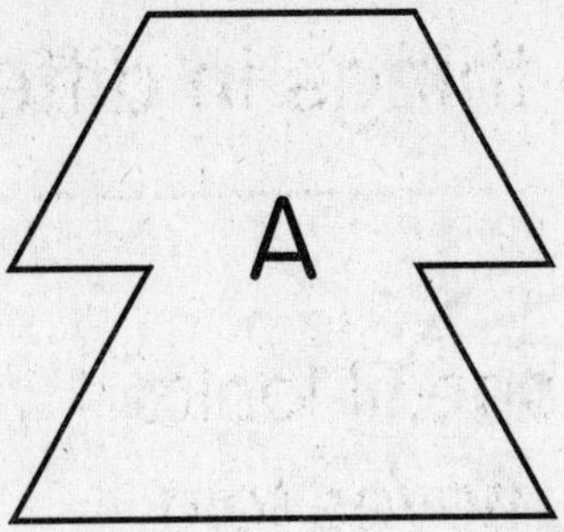

A

Unit: _____

Estimate: _____

Measure: _____

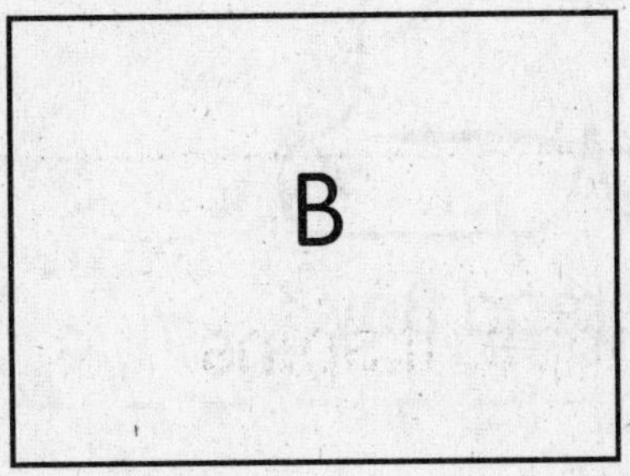

B

Unit: _____

Estimate: _____

Measure: _____

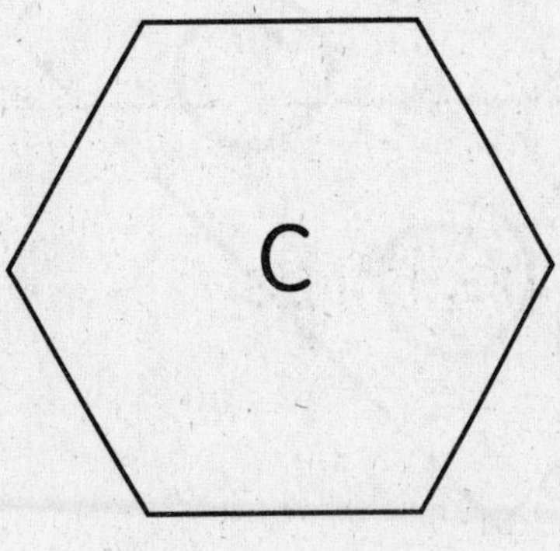

C

Cookies at the Bake Sale

Gingerbread Boy

Happy Face

Square Cookie

Gingerbread Girl

Comparing Cookies

Look at the cookies
for sale at the bake sale.

Gingerbread Boy   Happy Face

Estimate which cookie gives you more for
your money. _____

Measure the area of the cookies.
What unit did you use? _____
Record your results.

gingerbread-boy cookie	happy-face cookie

Explain which cookie gives you more for your money.

Cutting out Cookies

Use words and pictures to describe the cookie cutter.

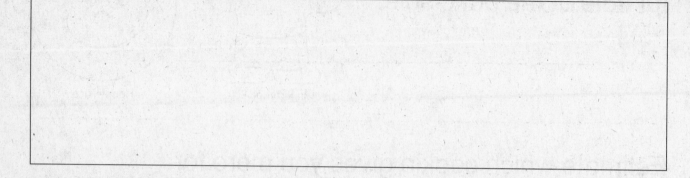

I estimate the area of the cookie dough is

_____ cookie cutters.

How did you solve the problem?

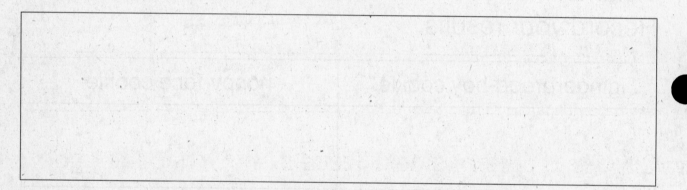

Compare your estimate with the actual area.

I used

☐ pictures

☐ numbers

☐ words

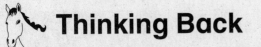 **Thinking Back**

● What questions can you ask to find out about
a 2-D shape?

_____

_____

_____

Describe 3 different ways to move a shape:

1. _____

2. _____

● 3. _____

Choose a pattern block. Trace it, move it to the right,
then trace it again.

🐴 Write About Math

Use pictures, numbers, and
words to show your thinking.

The answer is
36

What numbers can you add to make 36?

What numbers can you subtract to make 36?

Toss and Win

Toss your counters onto the board twice.
Add the numbers. What prize do you win?

| Small: Under 25 | Medium: 25–49 | Large: 50–75 | Jumbo: Over 75 |

23	11	32	38	19
42	27	45	13	33
49	51	36	58	16
6	47	28	41	21

Chapter 8 Lessons 1 and 2

Ways to Win

Write one way to win each prize.
Show how to add the numbers you chose.

Small Prize: Total is under 25.	**Medium Prize:** Total is 25 to 49.
Large Prize: Total is 50 to 75.	**Jumbo Prize:** Total is over 75.

Collections

Use blocks to solve each problem. Show what you did.

Lisa has 32 stuffed animals. Brandon has 37.
How many do they have altogether?

Malik has 39 coins. If he collects 25 more, how
many will there be?

Make up an adding problem about a collection.
Use 2-digit numbers. Then solve the problem.
Show what you did.

Glossary Word

regroup

When we **regroup**, we change the way we show a number with 10s and 1s to make it easier to add or subtract.

Draw 3 ways to make 36 with base ten blocks.
Circle a way that makes it easy to see how many blocks there are.

Underline a way that makes it easy to subtract 18.

Chapter 8 Lesson 3

Comparing Heights

Circle the name of the person in each box who is taller.

Show how to find the height difference.

Name	Height in Cubes
Liam	52
Sarah	55
Hayden	66
Michael	60
Maya	71
Maria	68
Trey	78
Zoe	70
Farhad	82
Eve	63

Zoe
Trey

Maria
Liam

Michael
Eve

Farhad
Sarah

Amazing Number Tricks

What can you add or subtract to change the first number into the second number?

Show how you know.

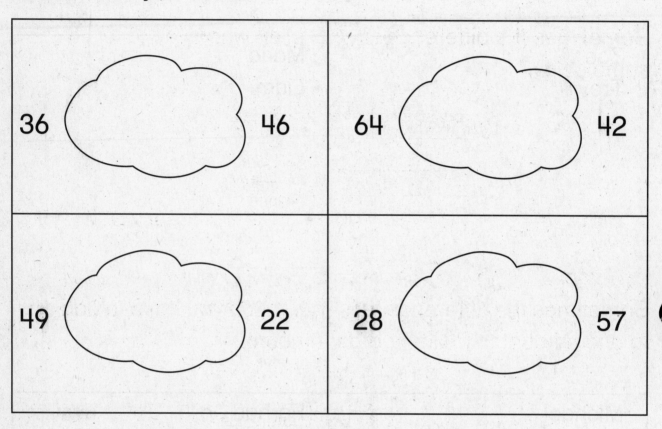

Choose numbers for each side of the cloud.
Show how to find out what changed.

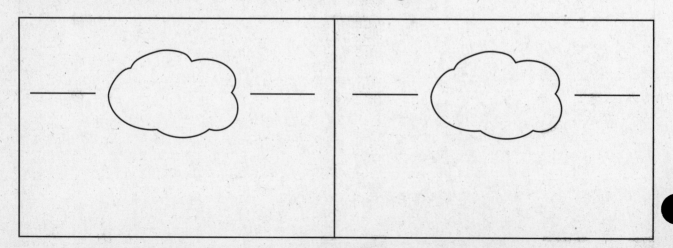

Chapter 8 Lesson 5

Glossary Words

difference

When you subtract, you start with a whole amount. Something happens to one part. You use subtraction to figure out the other part. The part you figure out is called the **difference**.

Sometimes the difference is what's left when you take some away.

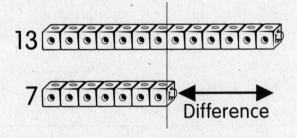

13 – 7 = _____

Sometimes the difference tells how much you have to add on to one amount to make another amount.

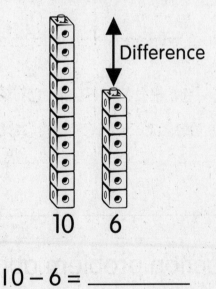

10 – 6 = _____

Chapter 8 Lesson 6   Activity 8.8

How Many Tickets?

Show one way to solve each problem.

A theatre sold 67 tickets to a show.
43 tickets were for children up to 12 years old.
How many were for people older than 12?

LaShawn won 72 tickets at the arcade.
She used 47 to buy a toy giraffe.
How many tickets does she have left?

Make up a subtraction problem about tickets.
Write it on another page.
Solve it. Show what you did.

Chapter 8 Lesson 7

Farmer Sue's Apples

● Show how to solve each problem.
Use pictures, numbers, and words.

On Monday, Farmer Sue took 69 apples to the market. She sold 48. How many apples were left?

On Tuesday, Farmer Sue picked 74 more apples. Now how many apples did she have?

On Wednesday, Farmer Sue took the apples to the market. She sold 67. How many apples did she have left?

I'm a Math Thinker

Colour and write to show the math thinking you used.

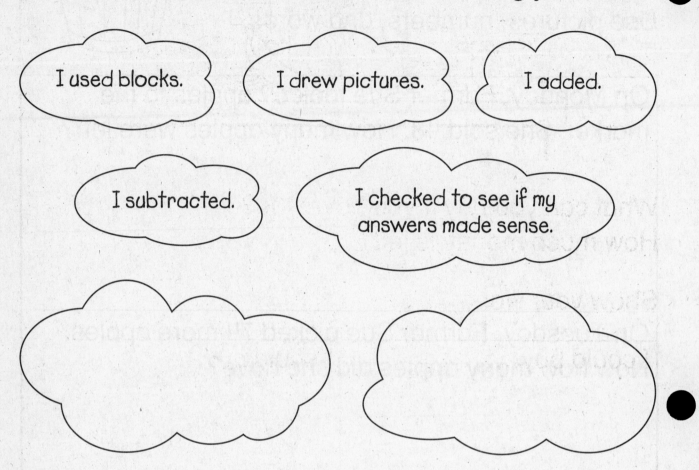

I used blocks.

I drew pictures.

I added.

I subtracted.

I checked to see if my answers made sense.

Write a problem about Farmer Sue's apples. Show how to solve your problem.

Snack Counter

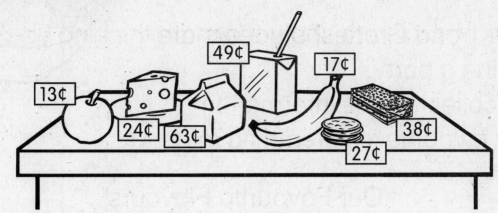

What can you buy if you have 90¢?
How much money is left?

Show your work.

I could buy…	I could buy…
I would have _____ ¢ left.	I would have _____ ¢ left.

Ice Cream

Grade 1 and Grade 2 students are
planning a party.
They collected this information
about favourite ice cream flavours.

Our Favourite Flavours

Flavour	Grade 1	Grade 2
chocolate	24	28
vanilla	25	29
strawberry	32	19
maple	19	25

Which 2 flavours should they serve at the party?

_____

Why shouldn't they serve maple ice cream at

the party? _____

_____

Use addition and subtraction to explain your choice.
Show your work. Use numbers, words, and pictures.

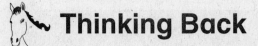 **Thinking Back**

● Choose 2 numbers between 25 and 70.

My numbers are _____ and _____.

Show how you can add these 2 numbers.

```

```

● Show how you can find the difference between
these 2 numbers.

```

```

● Explain your solutions to a partner.

Write About Math

Write about the pictures you found.
Show what things come in 2s, 3s, 5s, or 10s.
Each time, tell how many groups and how many items in all.

How Many Groups?

● Draw the groups and show how many in all. Write an addition sentence for your groups.

_____ groups of _____	_____ groups of _____
_____ groups of _____	_____ groups of _____
_____ groups of _____	_____ groups of _____

Making Arrays

My number is _____.

How can you show your number in equal rows? Draw and label it.

Show your number in as many ways as you can.

Glossary Words

multiply

You **multiply** when you join equal groups.

Here are 3 groups of 2 marbles. There are ＿＿ marbles.

divide

You **divide** when you separate a collection into equal groups or shares.

This is how 2 people would share 8 stickers fairly. Each person gets ＿＿ stickers.

Making It Fair

You and a friend each scoop a handful of cubes.
Show how many you each scooped.
Show how you made it fair.
Circle the handfuls that you can divide fairly.

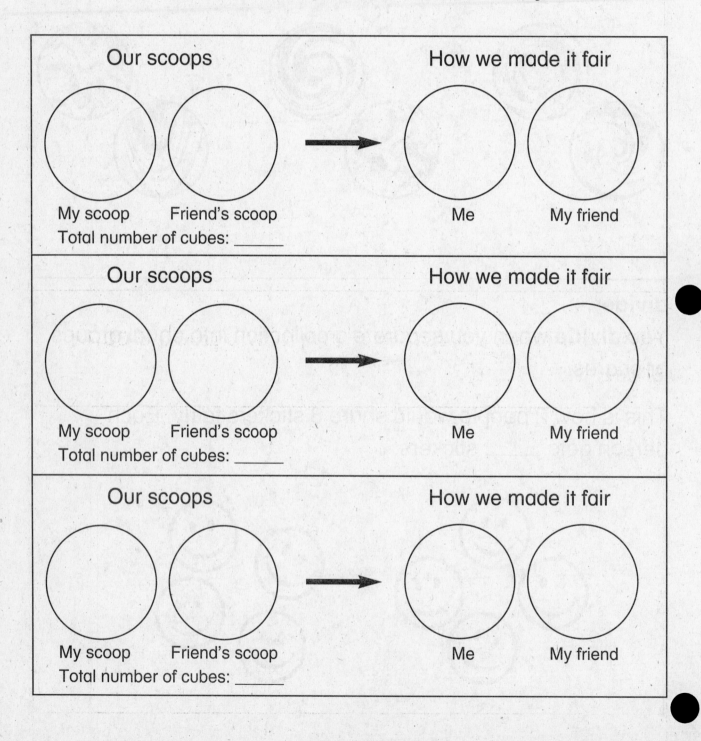

Sharing with My Friends

● You have 30 trading cards for 5 people to share.
Show how you can share the cards fairly.
Use words, pictures, and numbers.

●

Now you have 25 cards. Show how 5 people can
share them fairly.

●

Amusement Park

The ___ students in our class are going on each ride.

How many people are in each car?

How many cars do we fill?

How many people are left over?

How many people are in each swing?

How many swings do we fill?

How many people are left over?

How many people are in each teacup?

How many teacups do we fill?

How many people are left over?

How many people are in each car?

How many cars do we fill?

How many people are left over?

Chapter 9 Lesson 6

Sharing Stickers

 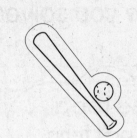  

Number of people	Number of stickers for each person	Any left over?
1		
2		
3		
4		
5		
6		
7		
8		

I'm a Math Thinker

Colour and write to show how you solved the problem. ●

I looked for a number pattern.

I made equal groups.

I used skip counting.

I made a chart.

Think of another problem you've solved that was like this one. Tell how the 2 problems are the same.

Chapter 9 Lesson 7

Making Space Creatures

● Draw your space creature.

● Are 20 toothpicks and 20 cubes enough for you to make 4 of your space creatures? Explain your answer.

I used
☐ pictures
☐ numbers
☐ words

Chapter 9 Chapter Task

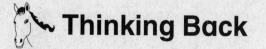

Start with 20 marbles.
Show the different ways to make gift bags with the same number of marbles in each one.

Write _____ sets of _____ for each of your answers.

Explain your thinking to a partner.

Write About Math

About what time do you usually eat lunch?

About how much time do you spend eating lunch?

Pretend you want soup for lunch at school. It costs 50¢. What coins can you use to pay?

How Old Am I?

My birth date is: _____.

A picture of me as a baby:

Today's date is: _____.

A picture of me today:

I am _____ years

      _____ months

      _____ days old.

Tell how you solved the problem.

Chapter 10 Lesson 1

Glossary Words

day

A **day** is a unit of time that is longer than an hour.

There are _____ hours in a day.

week

A **week** is a unit of time that is longer than a day.

There are _____ days in a week.

month

A **month** is a unit of time that is longer than a week.

There are about _____ weeks in a month.

I was born in the month of _____.

year

A **year** is a unit of time that is longer than a month.

There are _____ months in a year.

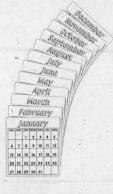

In a Minute

Activity	Estimate	Amount of Time

What I can do in …

Half an hour	I Hour

Glossary Words

minute

A **minute** is a unit of time.

I can do about _____
jumping jacks in 1 minute.

hour

An **hour** is a unit of time that is longer than a minute.

There are _____ minutes in 1 hour.

Time to the Quarter-Hour

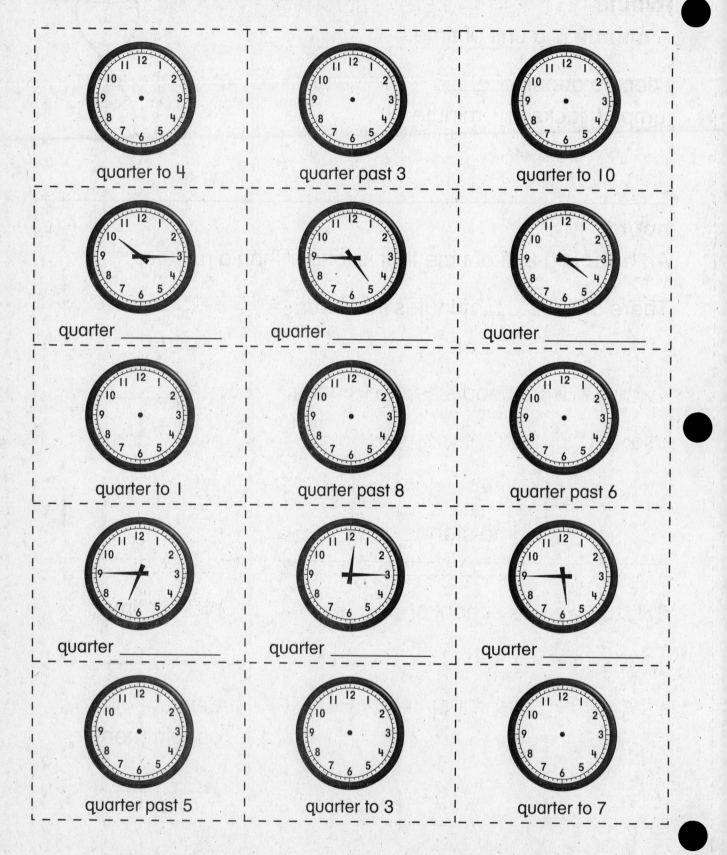

quarter to 4

quarter past 3

quarter to 10

quarter _____

quarter _____

quarter _____

quarter to 1

quarter past 8

quarter past 6

quarter _____

quarter _____

quarter _____

quarter past 5

quarter to 3

quarter to 7

Digital Time

● Read and finish the stories.

Colin left school at 3 o'clock to visit his grandmother. She was meeting him at 🕐. He went home for dinner at 🕕.	meet grandma _____:_____ dinner _____:_____
Prab went to bed at 🕗 so she would have a good sleep before the soccer game in the morning. Prab woke up at 🕖 and got ready for her game. The game started at 🕘.	bedtime _____:_____ soccer game _____:_____
Kazuo went to school at 🕘. His dad picked him up at 🕛 to go to the dentist. The appointment was at 🕐.	pick up time _____:_____ dentist appointment _____:_____

Counting Coins

Write your total in the box.

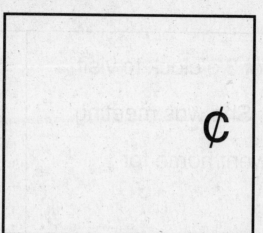

¢

Draw different ways to show the total.

Glossary Words

penny

A **penny** is a coin.

A penny is worth _____ ¢.

---

nickel

A **nickel** is a coin.

A nickel is worth _____ ¢.

---

dime

A **dime** is a coin.

A dime is worth _____ ¢.

---

quarter

A **quarter** is a coin.

A quarter is worth _____ ¢.

_____ pennies = 1 nickel

_____ nickels = 1 dime

_____ nickels = 1 quarter

_____ quarters = $1

At the Diner

What was your total? How much change did you get back from $1?

How did acting it out help you solve money problems?

Chapter 10 Lesson 7

The Three Coins Diner

● Draw items for your menu. Give each item a price you can pay for with 3 coins. Show on the clocks the time you got to the diner and the time you will leave.

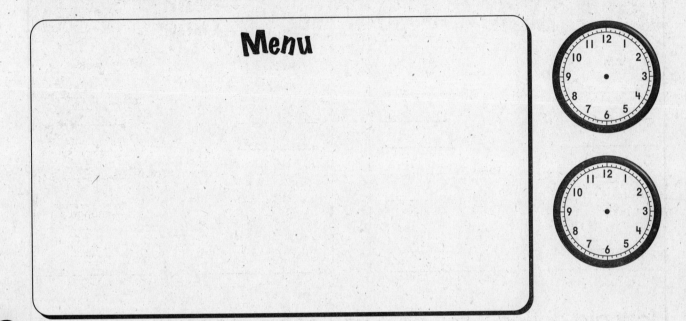

Menu

● Choose an item: _____

Show the 3 coins you need to pay for it.

_____   _____   _____

Show another way you can pay for it.

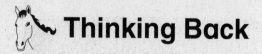
What I learned about telling time:

What I learned about using money:

Chapter 10 Chapter Task

Write About Math

Choose a 3-D shape.

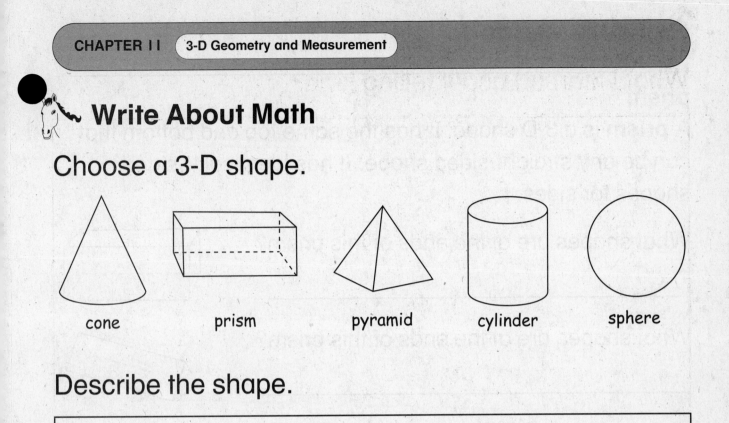

cone   prism   pyramid   cylinder   sphere

Describe the shape.

Tell how you can make the shape.

Glossary Words

prism

A **prism** is a 3-D shape. It has the same top and bottom that can be any straight-sided shape. It has identical 4-sided shapes for sides.

What shapes are at the ends of this prism?

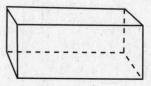

_____

What shapes are at the ends of this prism?

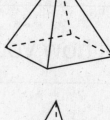

_____

pyramid

A **pyramid** is a shape with triangle sides that come together at a point. The bottom can be a square, a triangle, or another straight-sided shape.

What shape is on the bottom of this pyramid?

_____

What shape is on the bottom of this pyramid?

_____

Chapter 11 Lesson 1

Supermarket Display

● Draw a diagram of your supermarket display.
Label the diagram.

What shapes did you use to build your display?

My Shape Skeleton

This is my shape.

I used _____ to make the edges.

There are _____ edges in all.

I used _____ to make the vertices.

There are _____ vertices in all.

Glossary Words

 skeleton

A **skeleton** is a 3-D shape that has only edges and vertices.

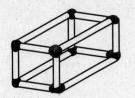

This is a skeleton of a _____.

Describing 3-D Shapes

Shape description:

Underline the math words you used.

Choose a different 3-D shape.

Draw	Describe

Underline the math words.

Chapter 11 Lesson 5

Making Models of 3-D Shapes

● Choose a 3-D shape from the poster. Draw the shape.

Build a model of the shape. Tell what your model looks like. Use numbers, words, and pictures.

Measuring Capacity

Container	Unit	Estimate	Capacity

Measure and record the capacity of each container.

Circle the container with the greatest capacity.

Underline the container with the least capacity.

Measuring Mass

 Measure and record the mass of each object.

Object	Unit	Estimate	Mass

Circle the heaviest object.

Underline the lightest object.

Comparing Mass

Units

Objects

Which One Is Mine?

● About the 3-D shape:

Faces	
Edges	
Vertices	

● About the mass:

One more thing about my shape:

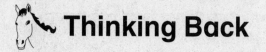
Choose a 3-D shape:

_____

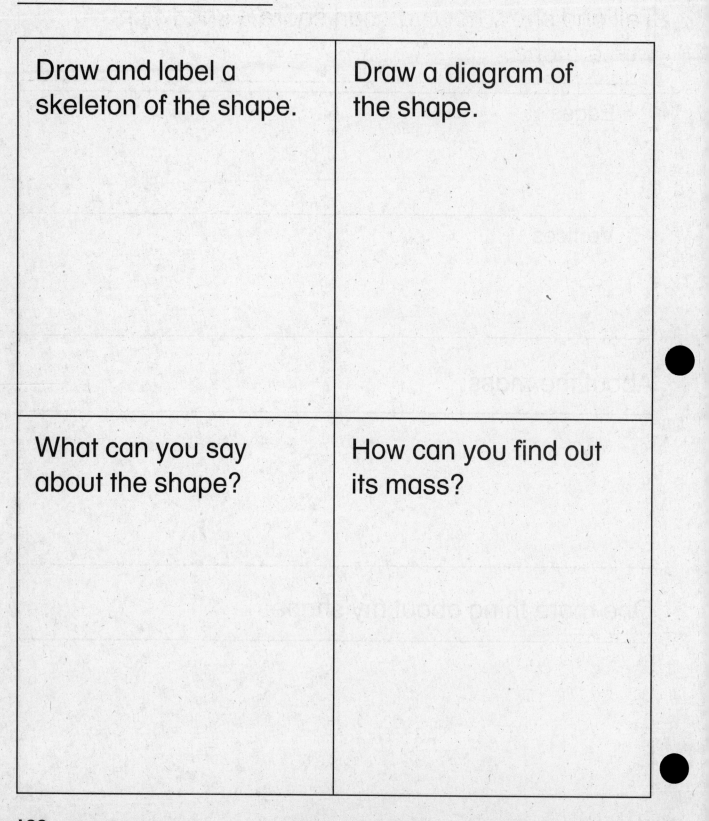

Draw and label a skeleton of the shape.	Draw a diagram of the shape.
What can you say about the shape?	How can you find out its mass?

Write About Math

Tell and show how you can share a sandwich
with a friend.

Making Shapes

Make a shape with 2 blocks that are the same.
Sketch your shape. Colour one half.

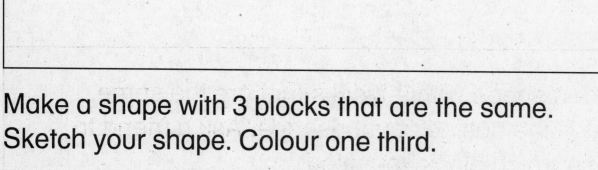

Make a shape with 3 blocks that are the same.
Sketch your shape. Colour one third.

Making More Shapes

● Make a shape with 4 blocks that are the same.
Sketch your shape. Colour one fourth.

● Make a shape with 4 blocks that are the same.
Sketch the outline of your shape. Ask a friend to
guess which block you used.

Glossary Words

half

When there are 2 equal parts, we say each part is a **half**.

Colour half of the heart. Then sketch your own shape and colour half of it.

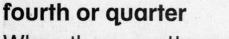

fourth or quarter

When there are 4 equal parts, we say each part is a **fourth**. **Quarter** is another name for a fourth.

Colour one fourth of the flag.

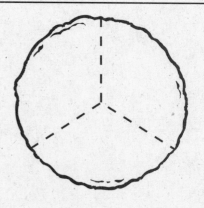

third

When there are 3 equal parts, we say each part is a **third**.

Colour one third of the cookie.

Chapter 12 Lesson 2

Sharing a Cake

How can Jacob show and explain how to share the cake with 3 friends?

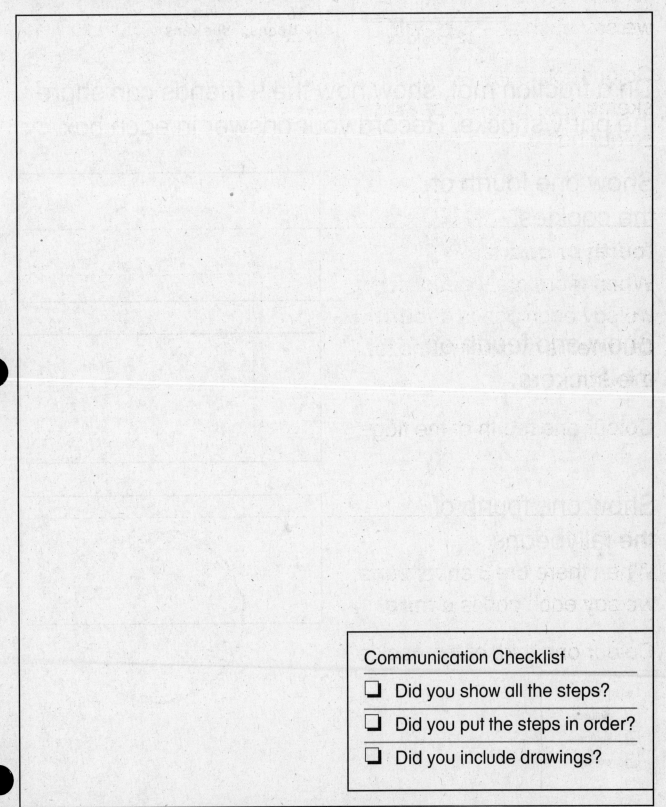

Communication Checklist

☐ Did you show all the steps?

☐ Did you put the steps in order?

☐ Did you include drawings?

Fair Shares

12 cookies   16 jelly beans   8 suckers

On a fraction mat, show how the 4 friends can share the party snacks. Record your answer in each box.

Show one fourth of the cookies.

Show one fourth of the suckers.

Show one fourth of the jellybeans.

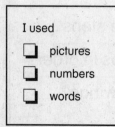

I used
- ☐ pictures
- ☐ numbers
- ☐ words

I'm a Math Thinker

● Colour and write to show how you solved the problem.

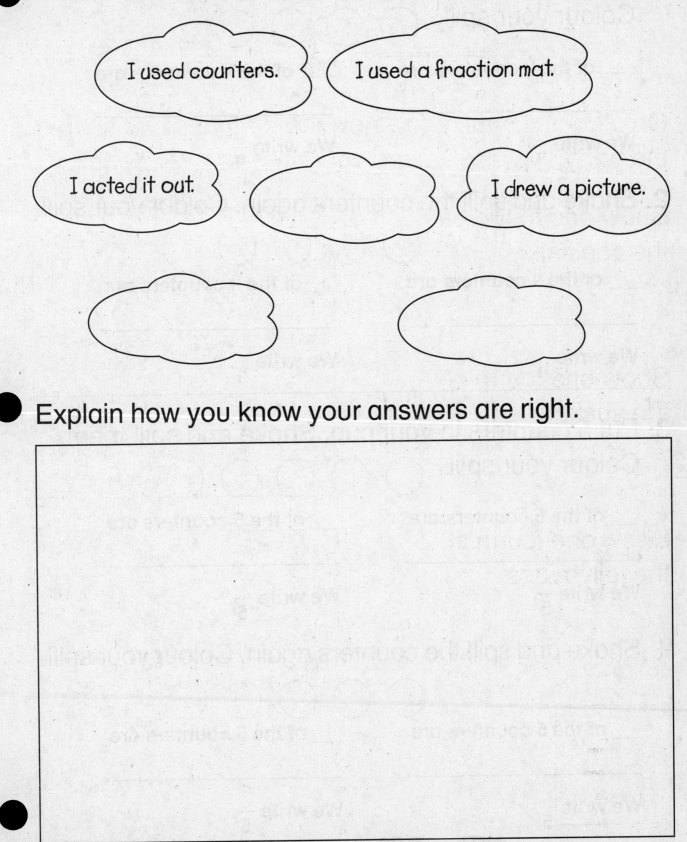

I used counters.

I used a fraction mat.

I acted it out.

I drew a picture.

● Explain how you know your answers are right.

Shake and Spill Fractions

1. Put 4 counters in your cup. Shake and spill them.
   Colour your spill. ◯ ◯ ◯ ◯

   ___ of the 4 counters are

   _____.

   We write $\frac{}{4}$.

   ___ of the 4 counters are

   _____.

   We write $\frac{}{4}$.

2. Shake and spill the counters again. Colour your spill.

   ◯ ◯ ◯ ◯

   ___ of the 4 counters are

   _____.

   We write $\frac{}{4}$.

   ___ of the 4 counters are

   _____.

   We write $\frac{}{4}$.

3. Put 5 counters in your cup. Shake and spill them.
   Colour your spill. ◯ ◯ ◯ ◯ ◯

   ___ of the 5 counters are

   _____.

   We write $\frac{}{5}$.

   ___ of the 5 counters are

   _____.

   We write $\frac{}{5}$.

4. Shake and spill the counters again. Colour your spill.

   ◯ ◯ ◯ ◯ ◯

   ___ of the 5 counters are

   _____.

   We write $\frac{}{5}$.

   ___ of the 5 counters are

   _____.

   We write $\frac{}{5}$.

Garden Problems

● This is what one third of the garden looks like: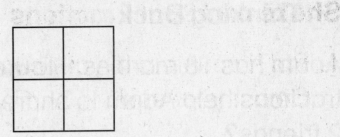

Draw a picture that shows what the whole garden might look like. Shade the part of your picture that shows one third.

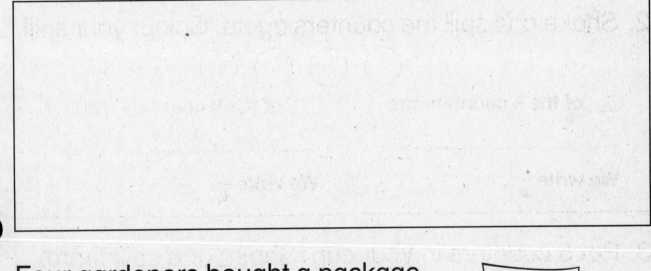

● Four gardeners bought a package of 24 seeds. The gardeners want to share the seeds fairly. How many seeds does each gardener get?

Thinking Back

Adam has 18 marbles. How can knowing about fractions help Adam to share his marbles with 2 friends?

Write About Math

Tell about an experiment you did.
Use words, pictures, and numbers.

In this experiment, I sometimes …

In this experiment, I never …

In this experiment, I always …

My Calendar

Think of at least 2 events for each section.

_____

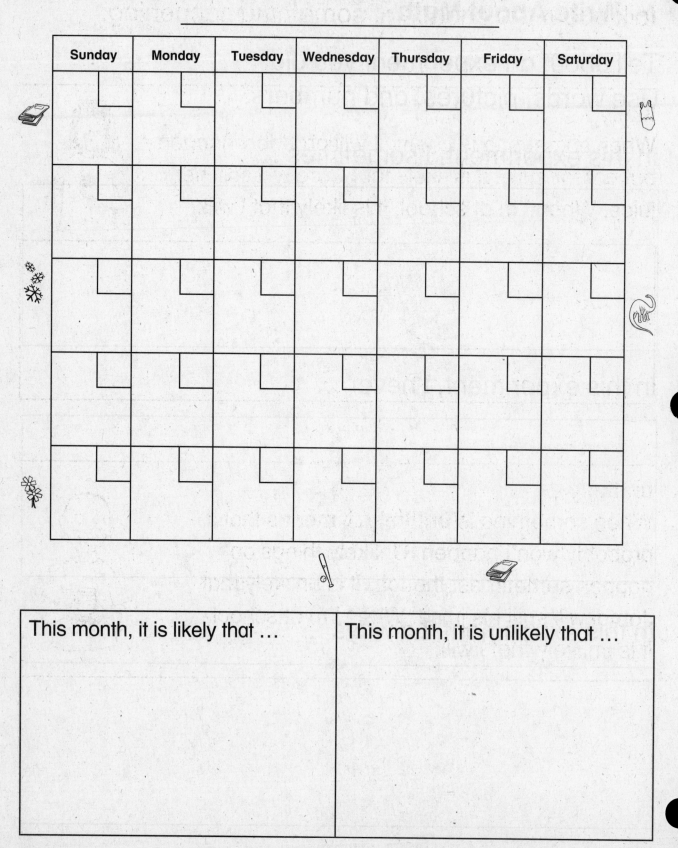

Sunday	Monday	Tuesday	Wednesday	Thursday	Friday	Saturday

This month, it is likely that …	This month, it is unlikely that …

Chapter 13 Lesson 1

Glossary Words

We use the words **unlikely**, **likely**, and **certain** to talk about the chance of something happening.

---

likely

When something is **likely**, it will probably happen but not for sure. It is likely that Cora will spill her juice. When I'm at school, it is likely that I will:

---

unlikely

When something is **unlikely**, it means that it probably won't happen. Unlikely things do happen sometimes, though. It is unlikely that Jamal will spill his juice. When I'm at school, it is unlikely that I will:

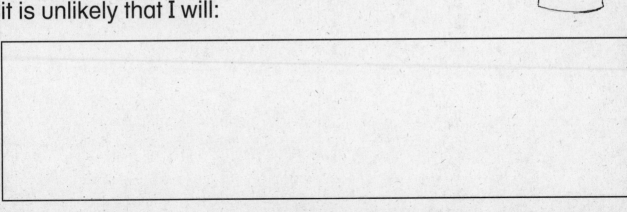

Glossary Words

certain

When something is **certain**,
it will happen for sure because
nothing else is possible. I am
certain that no one will spill this
juice. When I'm at school, it is
certain that I will:

Ups and Downs

1. How likely is it that the liquid
   in the thermometer will fall?
   Circle your prediction.

Impossible   Unlikely   Likely   Certain

Try the experiment. What happened?

2. How likely is it that the liquid
   in the thermometer will fall?
   Circle your prediction.

Impossible   Unlikely   Likely   Certain

Try the experiment. What happened?

More Ups and Downs

3. How likely is it that the liquid
   in the thermometer will rise?
   Circle your prediction.

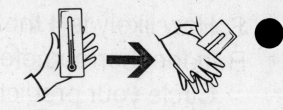

Impossible   Unlikely   Likely   Certain

Try the experiment. What happened?

4. How likely is it that the temperature in your hand is
   the same as that in your partner's hand?
   Circle your prediction.

Impossible   Unlikely   Likely   Certain

Try the experiment. What happened?

More Heads or More Tails?

Spill 3 coins out of a cup.
Repeat 20 times.

What do you think will happen?
❏ More spills will show "more heads."
❏ More spills will show "more tails."
❏ "More heads" and "more tails" will be the same.

Try the experiment. Tally your results.

More heads	More tails

We got more heads this many times: _____

We got more tails this many times: _____

My prediction was: Right _____Wrong _____

How Many Tries?

Keep rolling until you get a double.
Colour squares to keep track of the number of tries.

1. We predict that we will need _____ tries.

   Our tries

   It took _____ tries.

2. We predict that we will need _____ tries.

   Our tries

   It took _____ tries.

3. We predict that we will need _____ tries.

   Our tries

   It took _____ tries.

4. We predict that we will need _____ tries.

   Our tries

   It took _____ tries.

5. We predict that we will need _____ tries.

   Our tries

   It took _____ tries.

Doubles Experiment

● List the results of your doubles experiments in order from least to greatest.

———— , ———— , ———— , ———— , ———— , ———— ,

———— , ———— , ———— , ————

When you do the doubles experiment, it usually takes from ———— to ———— tries to get a double.

Circle the word that tells how likely it is that someone will roll doubles in just 3 tries.

Impossible   Unlikely   Likely   Certain

● Tell why you chose that word.

What Are the Numbers?

Pull out a card, look at it, and put it back.
Repeat with another card.
Card 1: _____ Card 2: _____
I predict the numbers in the bag might be:

Pull out 1 card. Record and tally the number.
Put the card back. Repeat 15 times.

Number	Number	Number	Number
_____	_____	_____	_____

Make a new prediction.
Use information from your experiment.

Explain how you made your prediction.

Look at the numbers.
Which ones match your prediction? _____

Describing an Experiment

● Spin 20 times.

Complete the tally chart to keep track of your results.

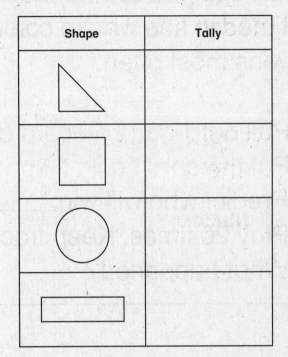

Shape	Tally

● Describe what happened.

Communication Checklist

❏ Did you use math language?

❏ Did you include enough information?

❏ Did you explain your thinking?

Chapter 13 Lesson 6   Activity 13.11

Who Will Win?

Zahra, Devon, and Luke are playing a game. They will spin the spinner 20 times to see whose colour wins most often.

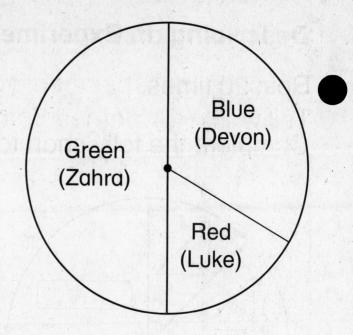

Predict who will win: _____
Play 20 times. Keep track of your results.
What happened?

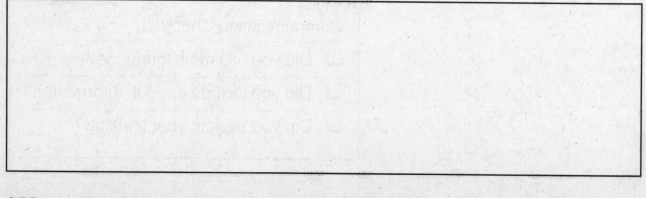

If you played again, who do you think would win? Explain.

Chapter 13 Chapter Task

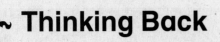

● Describe an experiment you did in this chapter.
Tell what you learned from the results.

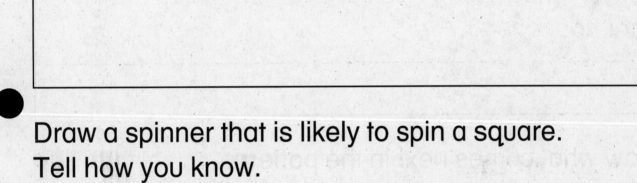

Draw a spinner that is likely to spin a square.
Tell how you know.

Write About Math

Draw the next 3 beads in the pattern.

I know because:

Show what comes next in the pattern.

I know because:

Wrapping-Paper Pattern

● Finish the pattern.

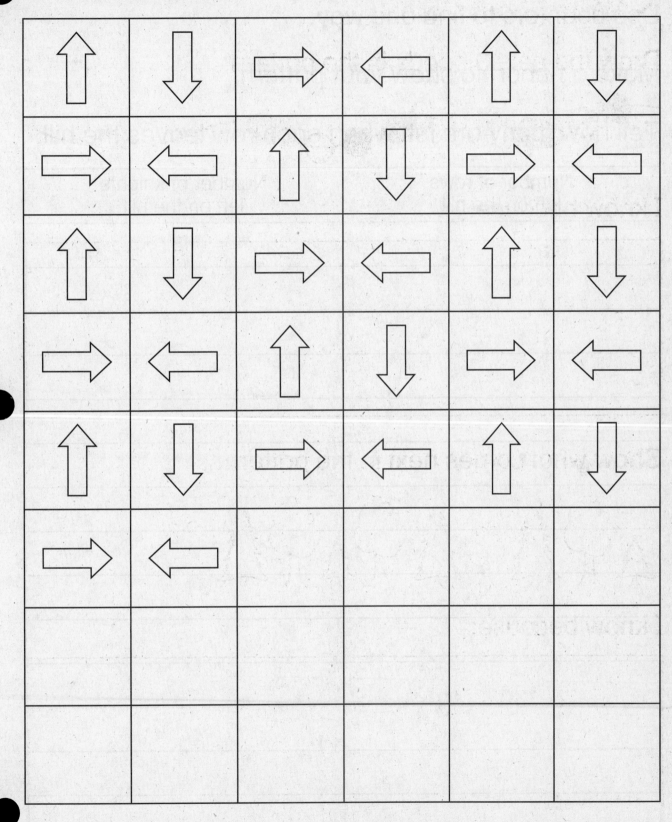

The Grand Old Duke of York

How can 48 knights march off the hill in equal rows?
Use counters to find one way.

Make a t-chart to show your pattern.

Tell how many are left when each row leaves the hill.

Number of rows left on the hill	Number of knights left on the hill
	48

Chapter 14 Lesson 3

Glossary Words

t-chart

A **t-chart** helps organize data so we can see patterns in the numbers. Keep the pattern going until this t-chart is filled.

Number of triangles	Number of corners
1	3
2	6
3	9
4	

How is the number of triangles changing? _____

How is the number of corners changing? _____

column and row

On a grid, we can talk about **rows** and **columns**.

Here is a row.

Here is a column.

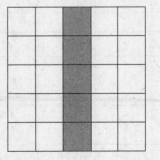

Colour a row orange. Colour a column blue.

Finish the Addition Table

+	0	1	2	3	4	5	6	7	8	9
0							6			
1							7			
2							8			
3							9			
4	4	5	6	7	8	9	10	11	12	13
5							11			
6							12			
7							13			
8							14			
9							15			

New Coats

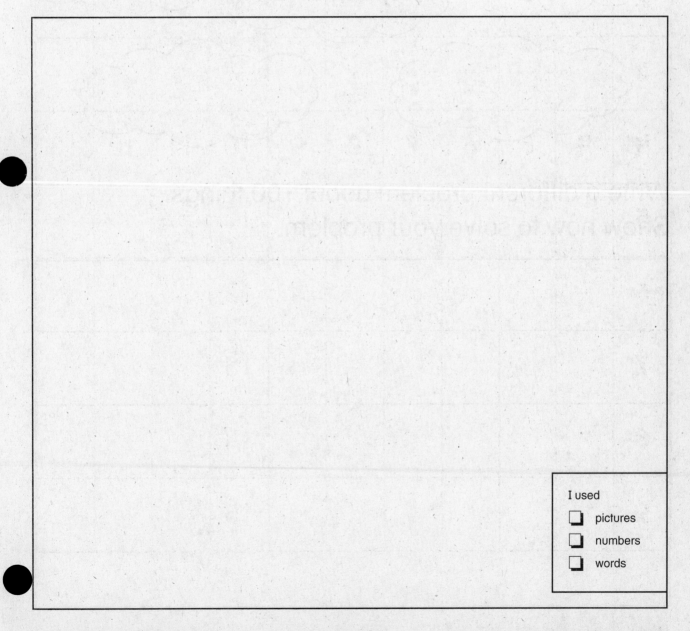

The Duke of York wants new coats
for 100 knights. Every 3rd knight
needs a red coat.
All the rest need blue coats.
How many more blue coats
than red coats should the Duke order?

Show how you solved the problem.

I used

☐ pictures

☐ numbers

☐ words

I'm a Math Thinker

Colour and write to show the math thinking you used.

I used a 100 chart.

I checked to see if my answer made sense.

I subtracted.

I found a pattern.

I added.

Write a different problem about 100 things.
Show how to solve your problem.

Chapter 14 Lesson 6

Making a Bead Pattern

● Here is the core of my bead pattern.

I repeated the core _____ times.

My bead chain will cost _____ .

●

●

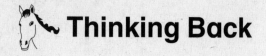

Thinking Back

I can explain any shape pattern using numbers.

Do you agree? Explain why or why not.

Make up an interesting number pattern.

What makes your pattern interesting?

Grade 2 Glossary

attribute

Activity 1.3

An **attribute** of an object tells something about that object.

Some attributes of this button are its
colour (it is grey)
shape (it is round)

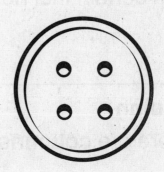

bar graph

Activity 3.3

A **bar graph** uses bars to show data.

This bar graph shows that 4 people said that hockey is their favourite sport. It also shows that more people like hockey than baseball.

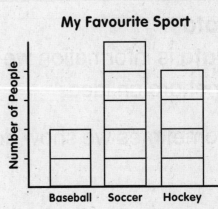

My Favourite Sport

Number of People

Baseball   Soccer   Hockey

centimetre

Activity 5.5

A **centimetre** is a unit of measure.

You can use centimetres to measure a pencil.

certain

Activity 13.4

When something is **certain**, it will happen for sure because nothing else is possible.

I am certain that no one will spill this juice.

column

Activity 14.4

There are **columns** on a grid.

This is a column.

data

Activity 3.3

Data is information we collect to answer a question or share an idea.

Sometimes we show data in graphs, tables, and charts.

day

Activity 10.3

A **day** is a unit of time that is longer than an hour.

There are 7 days in a week.

Glossary

difference

When you subtract, you start with a whole amount. Something happens to one part. You use subtraction to figure out the other part. The part you figure out is called the **difference**.

Sometimes the difference is what's left when you take some away.

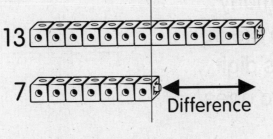

$$13 - 7 = 6$$

Sometimes the difference tells how much you have to add on to one amount to make another amount.

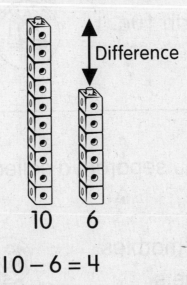

$$10 - 6 = 4$$

digit

Activity 6.5

The numbers from 0 to 9 are called **digits**.

We write all the numbers in our number system with these digits.

tens digit — ones digit

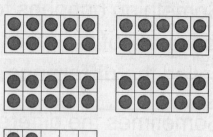

In greater numbers, the tens digit tells how many full 10-frames there are in a number. The ones digit tells how many extra ones there are.

dime

Activity 10.9

A **dime** is a coin worth 10¢.

divide

Activity 9.4

You **divide** when you separate a collection into equal groups or shares.

If 2 people share 10 marbles fairly, each person gets 5 marbles.

Glossary

estimate

Activity 2.3

An **estimate** tells about,
but not exactly, how many.

Estimate: 20
Count: 21

fact family

Activity 4.3

A **fact family** is a group of facts. Each fact uses
the same numbers.

These four facts make a fact family.

$$3 + 5 = 8 \qquad 8 - 5 = 3$$
$$5 + 3 = 8 \qquad 8 - 3 = 5$$

flips

Activity 7.8

If you **flip** a shape,
it flips across a line.

fourth or quarter

Activity 12.4

When there are 4 equal parts,
we say each part is a **fourth**.
Quarter is another name for a fourth.

One fourth of the door is shaded.

growing pattern

Activity 1.7

Growing patterns change in some sort of regular way.

Some growing patterns change by adding or subtracting the same number over and over:

2, 4, 6, 8, 10.

Some growing patterns change in other regular ways.

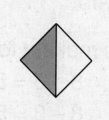

half

Activity 12.4

When there are 2 equal parts, we say each part is a **half**.

Half of the diamond is shaded.

height

Activity 5.2

When you measure **height**, you measure how tall something is, from top to bottom or bottom to top.

The flower is taller than the grass.
The flower is shorter than the tree.

hour

Activity 10.5

An **hour** is a unit of time that is longer than a minute.

Glossary

length

Activity 5.2

When you measure **length**, you measure how long something is, from beginning to end.

The marker is longer than the chalk.
The pen is longer than the marker.

likely

Activity 13.3

When something is **likely**, it will probably happen, but not for sure.

It is likely that Cora will spill her juice.

metre

Activity 5.5

A **metre** is 100 centimetres long.

minute

Activity 10.5

A **minute** is a unit of time.

There are 60 minutes in an hour.

month

Activity 10.3

A **month** is a unit of time that is longer than a week.

There are 12 months in a year.

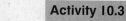

multiply

Activity 9.4

You **multiply** when you join equal groups.

Here are 3 groups of 2 marbles.

nickel

Activity 10.9

A **nickel** is a coin worth 5¢.

pattern core

Activity 1.3

The **pattern core** is the part of a pattern that keeps repeating.

Here is a pattern.   ○□△○□△○□△

This is its pattern core.   ○□△

penny

Activity 10.9

A **penny** is a coin worth 1¢.

Glossary

perimeter

Activity 5.5

The **perimeter** is the distance around a shape or object.

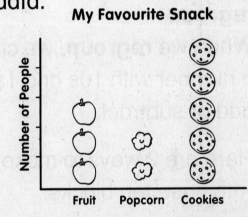

pictograph

Activity 3.3

A **pictograph** uses pictures to show data.

This pictograph shows that 3 people like fruit for a snack, 5 people like cookies for a snack, and 2 people like popcorn for a snack.

My Favourite Snack

prism

Activity 11.2

A **prism** is a solid shape with rectangular sides. The top and bottom can be rectangles, triangles, or another straight-sided shape.

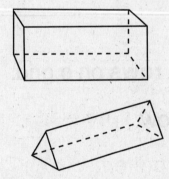

pyramid

Activity 11.2

A **pyramid** is solid shape with triangle sides that come together at a point. The bottom can be a square, a triangle, or another straight-sided shape.

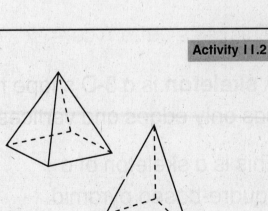

quarter

Activity 10.9

A **quarter** is a coin worth 25¢.

A quarter is also another name for a fourth.

regroup

Activity 8.5

When we **regroup**, we change the way we show a number with 10s and 1s to make it easier to add or subtract.

Here are 2 ways to make 27 with base ten blocks.

row

Activity 14.4

There are **rows** on a grid.

This is a row.

skeleton

Activity 11.5

A **skeleton** is a 3-D shape that has only edges and vertices.

This is a skeleton of a square-based pyramid.

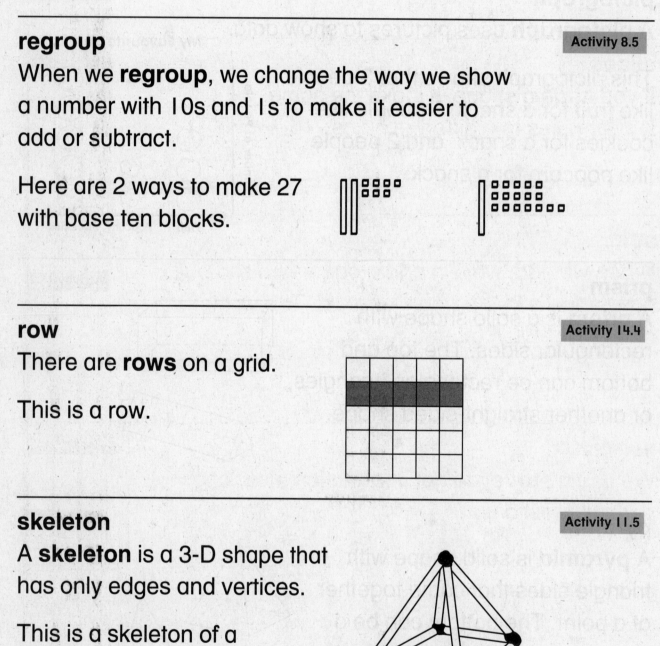

skip count

Activity 2.3

When we **skip count**, we count by leaving out the same size group of numbers each time.

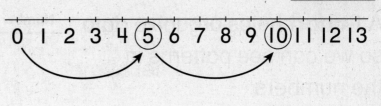

slides

Activity 7.8

If you **slide** a shape, it looks the same. It just moves to a different place.

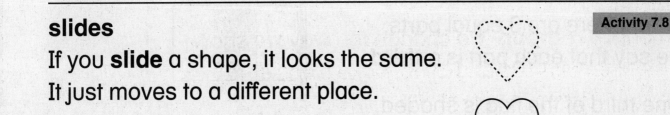

sum

Activity 4.3

When we add, we join parts together to find out how much is in the whole amount. The whole amount is called the **sum**.

survey

Activity 3.5

We use a **survey** to get information by asking people questions.

Glossary   **171**

t-chart

Activity 14.4

A **t-chart** helps organize data so we can see patterns in the numbers.

Number of Children	Number of Eyes
1	2
2	4
3	6
4	8

third

Activity 12.4

When there are 3 equal parts, we say that each part is a **third**.

One third of the flag is shaded.

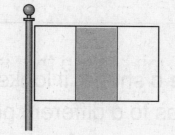

turns

Activity 7.8

If you **turn** a shape, it spins around a point.

unlikely

Activity 13.3

When something is **unlikely**, it means that it probably won't happen. Unlikely things do happen sometimes, though.

It is unlikely that Jamal will spill his juice.

Glossary

week

A **week** is a unit of time that is longer than a day.

A week has 7 days.

January

Sunday	Monday	Tuesday	Wednesday	Thursday	Friday	Saturday
		1	2	3	4	5
6	7	8	9	10	11	12
13	14	15	16	17	18	19
20	21	22	23	24	25	26
27	28	29	30	31		

year

A **year** is a unit of time that is longer than a month.

A year has 12 months.

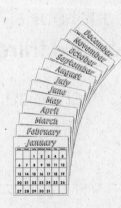

Glossary